The *Speedy* Revision Guide

Key Stage 4
GCSE Higher

Speedy Revision

Introduction

 This revision guide is aimed at candidates taking the Higher tier in GCSE Mathematics, and is suitable for all examination boards. It's the perfect size to keep with you at all times during the crucial weeks before the exams.

There is *speedy* coverage of each topic in the four main strands:
- Number
- Algebra
- Geometry & Measures
- Statistics & Probability

Everything you need to know about a topic is given on one or two pages, in the same format:
- **Essential facts**
  Everything you need to know, complete with examples.
- **Q & A**
  Easy-to-follow worked examples with clearly explained methods.
- **Check-up TESTs**
  To make sure everything has sunk in. (If you can do all the tests, you are heading in the right direction!)

On pages 117–118 there is a *speedy* revision test to check that you have remembered all the basic facts. (If you're short of time, try the revision test first, then revise those topics you got wrong; that truly is *speedy* revision!)

Good luck in your exams!

Contents

Non-calculator tricks

● **Multiplying by 10, 100, ...**
Move the digits <u>one place left</u> for <u>every zero</u> in 10, 100, ...

● **Dividing by 10, 100, ...**
Move the digits <u>one place right</u> for <u>every zero</u> in 10, 100, ...

➤ **Q & A**
a Multiply 2601.3582 by 100.
b Divide 72.618 by 1000.
Answer

a 2601.3582 $\xrightarrow{\times 100}$ 260135.82

Each digit moves <u>two places left</u>.

Place holders

b 72.618 $\xrightarrow{\div 1000}$ 0.072618

Each digit moves <u>three places right</u>.

➤ **Method**
❶ <u>Count</u> the number of <u>zeros</u> in 10 or 100 or ...
❷ <u>Move</u> the digits one place left/right <u>for every zero</u>. (Focus on a digit next to the decimal point to help you.)
❸ Use <u>zeros as place holders</u> if necessary.

Use your head.

● *Speedy* **non-calculator tricks**
To <u>add 9</u>, 99, 999, ... <u>add 10</u>, 100, 1000, ... <u>then subtract 1</u>.
To <u>subtract 9</u>, 99, 999, ... <u>subtract 10</u>, 100, 1000, ... <u>then add 1</u>.
To <u>multiply by 9</u>, multiply <u>by 10</u> then subtract the <u>original number</u>.
To <u>multiply by 11</u>, multiply <u>by 10</u> then add the <u>original number</u>.
To <u>multiply by 5</u>, 50, 500, ... <u>multiply by 10</u>, 100, 1000, ... <u>then halve</u>.
To <u>divide by 5</u>, 50, 500, ... <u>divide by 10</u>, 100, 1000, ... <u>then double</u>.
To <u>multiply by 2, 4</u>, 8, ... <u>double, double again</u>, double again, ...

---

1 Multiply 56 218.13 by **a** 10 **b** 1000 **c** 10 000.

2 Divide 3002.18 by **a** 100 **b** 100 000.

3 Use the '*Speedy* non-calculator tricks' to do these:
a 1268 − 99 **b** 380 × 5 **c** 15 × 8 **d** 800 ÷ 500 **e** 280 × 11

TEST

Written multiplication & division

● Multiplying decimals

When multiplying decimals, the answer will have the <u>same number of decimal places</u> as the total number of decimal places in the <u>numbers being multiplied</u>.

➤ Q & A

Work out 7.18 × 0.9.

Answer

❶ There are <u>three</u> decimal places in total in 7.18 and 0.9 (two in 7.<u>18</u> and one in 0.<u>9</u>).

❷ 718 × 9 = 6462
$$\begin{array}{r} 718 \\ \times\ \ 9 \\ \hline 6462 \\ {\scriptstyle 1\ 7} \end{array}$$

❸ So the answer is <u>6.462</u>.

Write the answer with three (from part ❶) decimal places.

➤ Method

❶ Count the <u>total</u> number of decimal places in the <u>numbers being multiplied</u>.

❷ Work out the multiplication without the decimal points.

❸ Put the number of decimal places you counted in ❶ into your answer.

● Dividing decimals

Make sure you keep the <u>decimal points lined up</u> when dividing decimals.

➤ Q & A

Work out 32.8 ÷ 5.

Answer

$$\begin{array}{r} 6.56 \\ 5\overline{)32.^{3}8^{2}0^{3}} \end{array}$$

Work out as normal, keeping the decimal points lined up.

32.8 ÷ 5 = <u>6.56</u>

You can convert a division by a decimal to division by a whole number by multiplying everything by 10, 100, 1000, etc.
For example, to work out 10.57 ÷ 0.7 you could work out 105.7 ÷ 7 instead.

● Estimating calculations

Always check answers to calculations by estimating.
For example, 7.18 × 0.9 is roughly 7 × 1 = 7.
Which isn't far off the answer in the first **Q & A**.

Always make an estimate

Work out: **a** 6.42 × 7   **b** 45.6 × 3.4   **c** 120.6 ÷ 9   **d** 23.76 ÷ 1.1

Special number sequences

● **Square numbers**

Square numbers are whole numbers multiplied by themselves.

nth term $= n^2$

$1^2 = 1$ $2^2 = 4$ $3^2 = 9$ $4^2 = 16$ $5^2 = 25$

● **Cube numbers**

Cube numbers are whole numbers multiplied by themselves twice.

nth term $= n^3$

$1^3 = 1$ $2^3 = 8$ $3^3 = 27$ $4^3 = 64$ $5^3 = 125$

● **Triangular numbers**

Start at 1 and add 2, then 3, then 4, ...

nth term $= \frac{1}{2}n(n + 1)$

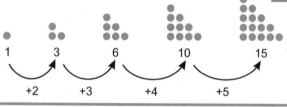

1   3   6   10   15

+2   +3   +4   +5

● **Powers of 2**

$2^1 = 2$, $2^2 = 4$, $2^3 = 8$, $2^4 = 16$, $2^5 = 32$, ...

nth term $= 2^n$

● **Powers of 10**

nth term $= 10^n$

$10^1 = 10$, $10^2 = 100$, $10^3 = 1000$, $10^4 = 10\,000$, $10^5 = 100\,000$, ...

---

1 What are the first ten **a** square **b** cube **c** triangular numbers?

2 What are the first ten **a** powers of 2 **b** powers of 10?

3 What is the nth term of the sequence of
a even numbers **b** odd numbers?   Close this page first!

4 Write down the nth terms of the above five sequences.

TEST

Prime numbers

● Prime numbers

> A prime number has exactly two factors (itself and 1).

Note: 1 is not a prime number (it has only one factor – itself).

You should memorise the first few primes:

2, 3, 5, 7, 11, 13, 17, 19, 23, ...

● Is it prime?

To check if a number is prime, all you have to do is divide by primes that are smaller than the square root of the number in question.

➤ Q & A

Is 67 a prime number?

Answer

❶ The square root of 67 is a bit more than 8 (use a calculator or the fact that $8^2 = 64$).

❷ So you only have to divide by 2, 3, 5 and 7.

$67 \div 2 = $ not a whole number

$67 \div 3 = $ not a whole number

$67 \div 5 = $ not a whole number

$67 \div 7 = $ not a whole number

❸ None of them divide into it exactly, so 67 is a prime number.

➤ Method

❶ Work out the square root of the number.

❷ Divide by all the primes that are smaller than the square root.

❸ If none of them divide into the number exactly, then the number is prime.

❹ If any of them divide into the number exactly, then the number is NOT prime.

---

1 Work out all the prime numbers less than 50.

2 Are these prime numbers? **a** 2546 **b** 2404 **c** 8765
How could you tell by just looking at the last digits?

3 'A number is divisible by 3 if the sum of its digits is divisible by 3.'
Use this fact to work out whether or not these numbers are prime: **a** 216 **b** 1953 **c** 177 147

TEST

Multiples, factors & prime factorisation

● Multiples

The multiples of a number are the numbers in its times-table.

> ➤ The multiples of 14 are 14, 28, 42, ...

● Factors

The factors of a number are the numbers that divide into it exactly.

To find all the factors of the number, start at 1 and divide by each whole number in turn. Stop when you get a repeat.

Factors always appear in pairs, i.e. 1 × 15 = 15 and 3 × 5 = 15.

> ➤ **The factors of 15**
>
> $15 ÷ 1 = 15$
>
> $15 ÷ 2 =$ not a whole number
>
> $15 ÷ 3 = 5$
>
> $15 ÷ 4 =$ not a whole number
>
> $15 ÷ 5 = 3$ (Repeats, so stop)
>
> So the factors of 15 are
> 1, 3, 5, and 15.

● Prime factorisation

This means 'break a number into its prime factors, and write them multiplied together'.

> ➤ **Q & A**
>
> Express 60 as a product of its prime factors.
>
> Answer
>
> $60 = 6 × 10$
>
> $= 2 × 3 × 10$
>
> $= 2 × 3 × 2 × 5$
>
> All the factors are now primes, so you can't break it down any further.

> ➤ **Method**
>
> ❶ Break the number into pairs of factors.
> ❷ Stop when all the factors are primes.
> ❸ Rewrite the prime factors in order of size (smallest first).
> ❹ Express any repeated prime factors using indices.

$= 2 × 2 × 3 × 5$ [rewrite the factors in order of size]

$= 2^2 × 3 × 5$ [write the answer with indices]

---

1 What are the first five multiples of **a** 7 **b** 12 **c** 21 **d** 104?
2 List all the factors of **a** 24 **b** 56 **c** 98.
3 Express these numbers as products of their prime factors:
    a 64 **b** 81 **c** 456 **d** 1225 **e** 2310

LCM & HCF

● Least common multiple

The least common multiple (LCM) is the smallest number that is a multiple of two or more numbers.

To find the LCM of two numbers you could list the multiples of both numbers, then pick out the smallest number that's in both lists. But this can take absolutely ages, so use the prime factorisation method below, it's much quicker.

➤ Q & A

What is the LCM of 15 and 42?

Answer

Prime factorisations are:

$15 = 3 \times 5$

$42 = 2 \times 3 \times 7$

So LCM = $2 \times 3 \times 5 \times 7 = 210$

3 appears in both prime factorisations but only include it once.

➤ Method

❶ Write each number as a product of its prime factors.

❷ Combine the prime factorisations, counting common factors only once.

❸ Multiply to get the LCM.

● Highest common factor

The highest common factor (HCF) is the largest number that is a factor of two or more numbers.

To find the HCF of two numbers you could list the factors of both numbers, then pick out the largest number that's in both lists. But again this can take absolutely ages, so use the prime factorisation method below, it's again much quicker.

➤ Q & A

What is the HCF of 720 and 84?

Answer

Prime factorisations are:

$720 = 2 \times 2 \times 2 \times 2 \times 3 \times 3 \times 5$

$84 = 2 \times 2 \times 3 \times 7$

So HCF = $2 \times 2 \times 3 = 12$

➤ Method

❶ Write each number as a product of its prime factors.

❷ Pick out all the prime factors common to both prime factorisations.

❸ Multiply them together to get the HCF.

---

1 What is the LCM of **a** 16 and 36 **b** 50 and 95?
2 What is the HCF of **a** 36 and 48 **b** 820 and 252?
3 Give the LCM and HCF of 12, 42 and 56.

TEST

Fractions (1)

● Equivalent fractions

You can find <u>equivalent fractions</u> by <u>multiplying/dividing</u> top and bottom by the <u>same number</u>.

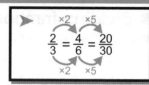

$$\frac{2}{3} = \frac{4}{6} = \frac{20}{30}$$

● Simplifying fractions

To write a fraction in its simplest form <u>divide numerator and denominator</u> (top and bottom) by the <u>highest common factor</u>.

This is often called '<u>cancelling</u>'.

$$\frac{15}{45} = \frac{1}{3}$$

15 is the HCF of 15 and 45.

● Adding/subtracting fractions

You can only add/subtract fractions once they have the <u>same denominator</u>.

$$\frac{2}{3} + \frac{1}{5} = \frac{10}{15} + \frac{3}{15} = \frac{10+3}{15} = \frac{13}{15}$$

● Multiplying fractions

Much easier than adding or subtracting – <u>don't worry about the denominators (just multiply them)</u>.

➤ Q & A

Work out $\frac{5}{6} \times \frac{2}{7}$.

Answer

$$\frac{5}{6} \times \frac{2}{7} = \frac{5 \times 2}{6 \times 7} = \frac{10}{42} = \frac{5}{21}$$

Always simplify your answer

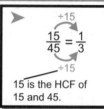

➤ Method

❶ <u>Multiply numerators</u>.
❷ <u>Multiply denominators</u>.
❸ <u>Simplify</u> if possible.

Sometimes you can make it easier by <u>cancelling out common factors</u>:

➤ Example

$$\frac{9}{10} \times \frac{15}{36} = \frac{\overset{1}{9}}{10} \times \frac{15}{\underset{4}{36}} = \frac{\overset{1}{9}}{\underset{2}{10}} \times \frac{\overset{3}{15}}{\underset{4}{36}} = \frac{1 \times 3}{2 \times 4} = \frac{3}{8}$$

9 is a common factor of 9 and 36, so you can cancel these out (there is 1 nine in 9 and 4 nines in 36).

5 is a common factor of 10 and 15, so you can cancel these out (there are 2 fives in 10 and 3 fives in 15).

Fractions (2)

● Dividing fractions

To divide fractions, you <u>turn the second one over then multiply</u>.

➤ $\frac{2}{9} \div \frac{3}{7} = \frac{2}{9} \times \frac{7}{3} = \frac{14}{27}$

● Improper & mixed fractions

<u>Improper fractions</u> are 'top heavy', i.e. the numerator is bigger than the denominator.
<u>Mixed numbers</u> are made up of a <u>whole number</u> and a <u>fraction</u>.

➤ $\frac{8}{5}$ is an improper fraction.
$3\frac{3}{5}$ is a mixed number.

● Fraction of

To work out a fraction of an amount treat the word '<u>of</u>' like a multiplication sign.

➤ **Example**
$\frac{2}{3}$ of £60 means $\frac{2}{3} \times$ £60
= £60 × 2 ÷ 3 = £40

● Fractions on your calculator

Your calculator should have a button that looks like **ab%** or **▤**.

To work out $\frac{2}{9} \div \frac{3}{7}$ press **2** **ab%** **9** **÷** **3** **ab%** **7** **=** to get

| $14\lrcorner27$ | in your display. This means the answer is $\frac{14}{27}$.

Or you may have to enter the fractions by pressing **▤** first, then use arrow keys to input the numbers. Your display will then look like this:

$\frac{14}{27}$.

Make sure you know how to enter fractions on <u>your</u> calculator.

---

1 Work these out, giving all answers in their simplest form:

a $\frac{3}{6} + \frac{1}{6}$ **b** $\frac{5}{8} - \frac{3}{8}$ **c** $\frac{2}{5} + \frac{3}{10}$ **d** $\frac{5}{12} - \frac{3}{8}$ **e** $\frac{3}{7} + \frac{3}{8}$

f $\frac{5}{12} \times \frac{3}{7}$ **g** $\frac{4}{7} \div \frac{5}{14}$ **h** $\frac{3}{8} \times \frac{4}{6}$ **i** $\frac{2}{5} \div \frac{4}{15}$ **j** $\frac{3}{10} \times \frac{25}{36}$

2 Convert these to improper fractions: **a** $3\frac{1}{5}$ **b** $4\frac{3}{8}$

3 Convert these to mixed numbers: **a** $\frac{41}{5}$ **b** $\frac{61}{8}$

4 Find: **a** $\frac{3}{5}$ of £55   **b** $\frac{5}{7}$ of £63   **c** $\frac{3}{4}$ of 12 400 kg

5 Check your answers to **Q1** on a calculator.

TEST

Fractions, decimals & percentages (1)

● Equivalents you should know

$\frac{1}{2} = 0.5 = 50\%$ $\frac{1}{10} = 0.1 = 10\%$ $\frac{1}{3} = 0.333... = 33\frac{1}{3}\%$

$\frac{1}{4} = 0.25 = 25\%$ $\frac{1}{100} = 0.01 = 1\%$ $\frac{2}{3} = 0.666... = 66\frac{2}{3}\%$

$\frac{3}{4} = 0.75 = 75\%$ $\frac{1}{8} = 0.125 = 12.5\%$ $\frac{1}{5} = 0.2 = 20\%$

● Converting fractions to decimals

To change a fraction to a decimal you <u>divide the numerator by the denominator</u>.

➤ **Q & A**

Convert $\frac{27}{40}$ to a decimal.

Answer

$27 \div 40 = 0.675$

➤ **Method**

❶ Write the fraction as a <u>division</u>.

❷ Divide using a <u>written method</u> or a <u>calculator</u> if necessary.

● Converting decimals to fractions

If there is <u>one decimal place</u>, write it <u>over 10</u>.

If there are <u>two decimal places</u>, write them <u>over 100</u>.

➤ **Examples**

$0.8 = \frac{8}{10} = \frac{4}{5}$

$0.12 = \frac{12}{100} = \frac{3}{25}$

Simplify fractions when possible.

This method can be extended to any number of decimal places.

➤ **Example**

$0.2957 = \frac{2957}{10\,000}$

● Converting percentages to decimals

This is pretty simple, just <u>divide by 100</u>. Remember to <u>get rid of the % symbol</u>. (See page 4 for the <u>easy</u> way to divide by 100.)

➤ **Example**

$15\% = 15 \div 100 = 0.15$

● Converting decimals to percentages

<u>Multiply</u> the decimal <u>by 100%</u>.

(See page 4 for the <u>easy</u> way to multiply by 100.)

➤ **Example**

$0.32 = 0.32 \times 100\% = 32\%$

Fractions, decimals & percentages (2)

● **Converting** fractions **to percentages**

Do this in two steps: fraction → decimal → percentage.

➤ **Q & A**

Convert $\frac{1}{8}$ to a percentage.

Answer

$\frac{1}{8} = 0.125 = 0.125 \times 100\% = \underline{12.5\%}$

➤ **Method**

❶ Convert to a decimal.

❷ Multiply by 100%.

● **Converting percentages to** fractions

Write the percentage as a fraction with denominator 100.

This is because '%' means out of 100.

➤ $40\% = \frac{40}{100} = \frac{2}{5}$ Simplify if you can.

● **Ordering** fractions**, decimals & percentages**

➤ **Q & A**

Order this list, smallest first.

1.3, 115%, 225%, $1\frac{1}{3}$

Answer

1.30, 1.15, 2.25, 1.33...

1.30, 1.15, 1.33..., 2.25

1.15, 1.30, 1.33..., 2.25

115%, 1.3, $1\frac{1}{3}$, 225%

➤ **Method**

❶ Convert any fractions or percentages to decimals.

❷ Compare whole numbers. Order the list by these.

❸ If several have the same whole number, order these by tenths.

❹ Repeat for hundredths, thousandths and so on.

❺ Rewrite the list with the original fractions & percentages in place.

---

1 Convert these to decimals: **a** $\frac{3}{8}$ **b** $\frac{12}{40}$ **c** $\frac{13}{125}$

2 Convert these to fractions: **a** 0.6 **b** 0.15 **c** 0.153

3 Convert these to decimals: **a** 35% **b** 57% **c** 8%

4 Convert these to percentages: **a** 0.45 **b** 0.67 **c** 0.3

5 Convert these to percentages: **a** $\frac{3}{5}$ **b** $\frac{3}{25}$ **c** $\frac{13}{20}$

6 Convert these to fractions: **a** 21% **b** 5% **c** 35%

7 Write these in order, smallest first: 4.2, 145%, 3.45, $4\frac{1}{8}$

TEST

Terminating & recurring decimals

● Terminating decimals

Fractions (in simplest form) with denominators whose only prime factors are 2 and 5 <u>terminate</u>. All others <u>recur</u>.

> $\frac{1}{40}$ = 0.025 terminates
>
> $40 = 2^3 \times 5$

● Recurring decimals

The shorthand way of writing recurring decimals is to <u>put dots</u> <u>over the first and last digits in the repeating group</u>.

> $0.\dot{3}$ means 0.333333...
> $0.\dot{6}\dot{2}$ means 0.626262...

● Converting a recurring decimal to a fraction

◆ To convert a <u>terminating decimal</u> to a fraction you put the significant figures over an appropriate power of 10, i.e. $0.72 = \frac{72}{100}$.

◆ Converting a <u>recurring decimal</u> to a fraction isn't quite so easy:

> **Q & A** (Classic exam question)
> Convert 0.363636... to a fraction.
> **Answer**
>
> Let $x = 0.363636...$ ❶
> Then $100x = 36.3636...$ ❷
> So $100x - x = 36$ [❷ − ❶]
> Therefore $99x = 36$
> So $x = \frac{36}{99} = \frac{4}{11}$

> **Method**
> ❶ Write $x = $ <u>original number</u>.
> ❷ Multiply by 10 or 100, ... to get <u>repeating part</u> in front of <u>decimal point</u>.
> ❸ Subtract equation ❶ from equation ❷.
> ❹ Rewrite as $x = $ 'fraction'.
> ❺ <u>Cancel down</u> if possible.

The quick way to answer the above type of **Q & A** is to write the repeating digits over the same number of 9s, for example:

$0.777... = \frac{7}{9}$ $0.454545... = \frac{45}{99} = \frac{5}{11}$ $0.\dot{3}45\dot{6} = \frac{3456}{9999} = \frac{384}{1111}$

<u>Be careful</u> though as this <u>quick method doesn't work</u> when there are digits at the start of the decimal that are <u>not repeated</u>, e.g. 0.4652525252... In this case you have to let $x = 0.46\dot{5}\dot{2}$ and work out $10\,000x - 100x$ (giving $x = \frac{2303}{4950}$).

Negative numbers

● Adding and subtracting

Use a <u>number line</u> to help you <u>add or subtract negative numbers</u>.

➤ **Q & A**   What is 3 – 7?

Answer

Start at 3 and count
back 7 places, giving
an answer of <u>–4</u>.

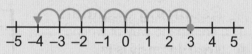

➤ **Q & A**   What is –3 – (–8)?

Answer

First of all deal with the 'minus minus'; together they make a plus.

So –3 – (–8) = –3 + 8

Start at –3 and count
forward 8 places, giving
an answer of <u>5</u>.

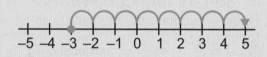

● Multiplying and dividing

Remember these rules for multiplying or dividing negative numbers.

❶ If the <u>signs are the same</u>, the answer is <u>positive</u> (+ + or – – is +).
❷ If the <u>signs are different</u>, the answer is <u>negative</u> (+ – or – + is –).

> ➤ **Examples**
>
> | The signs are the <u>same</u>: | $+6 \times +2 = +12$ | $+6 \div +2 = +3$ |
> |---|---|---|
> | | $-6 \times -2 = +12$ | $-6 \div -2 = +3$ |
> | The signs are <u>different</u>: | $-6 \times +2 = -12$ | $-6 \div +2 = -3$ |
> | | $+6 \times -2 = -12$ | $+6 \div -2 = -3$ |

● The sign change button

Your calculator will have a button like one of these: **+/−** **(−)**.
Make sure you know how to <u>enter negative numbers</u> with it.

---

1 Put these in order, smallest first: 2, 0, –4, –5, 3
2 Work these out and then check your answers on a calculator:
   a 3 – 6   **b** –14 – 12   **c** –34 – (–54)
   d 24 ÷ –6   **e** –5 × –6   **f** –12 × 12

TEST

Powers & roots (1)

● Powers

Powers are just a short way of writing repeated multiplication.

The 'power' or 'index' tells you how many times the number appears in the repeated multiplication.

> **➤ Example**
>
> $5^4 = 5 \times 5 \times 5 \times 5 = 625$
>
> The power is 4, so 5 appears 4 times.
>
> 5^4 is '5 to the power of 4'.

● Special powers

Any non-zero number 'to the power of 0' is 1.

Any number 'to the power of 1' is itself.

> **➤ Examples**
>
> $1^0 = 1$, $2^0 = 1$, $9^0 = 1$
>
> $1^1 = 1$, $2^1 = 2$, $5^1 = 5$

● Square and cube roots

Finding the root is the opposite (or inverse) of finding the power.

'What is the square root of 16?' means the same as 'What number squared is 16?'

> **➤ Example**
>
> $\sqrt{16} = 4$ or -4
>
> as $4 \times 4 = 16$
>
> and $-4 \times -4 = 16$

➤ Q & A

What is $\sqrt[3]{125}$?

Answer

This is the short way of writing 'What number is the cube root of 125?'

So ask yourself 'What number cubed is 125?'

The answer to this is 5:

$5 \times 5 \times 5 = 125$, so $\sqrt[3]{125} = 5$

➤ Method

❶ Check whether you are taking the square or cube root.

❷ Ask yourself what number squared/cubed gives the number in the question.

❸ Remember that square roots can be negative.

● Negative powers

A negative power is the reciprocal of a positive power.

('Reciprocal' just means 'one over'.)

> **➤ Examples**
>
> $5^{-4} = \frac{1}{5^4} = \frac{1}{625}$
>
> $6^{-1} = \frac{1}{6^1} = \frac{1}{6}$

Speedy Revision

Powers & roots (2)

● Working with powers

◆ To <u>multiply powers</u> of the same number <u>add the indices</u>.

◆ To <u>divide powers</u> of the same number <u>subtract the indices</u>.

◆ To take the <u>power of a power</u> <u>multiply the indices</u>.

> **Examples**
$$4^2 \times 4^3 = 4^{2+3} = 4^5$$
$$3^7 \div 3^4 = 3^{7-4} = 3^3$$
$$(10^2)^6 = 10^{2 \times 6} = 10^{12}$$

> **Q & A** What is $12^9 \div 12^7$?
Answer
$12^9 \div 12^7 = 12^{9-7} = 12^2 = \underline{144}$

> **Method**
❶ Use the <u>above rules</u> to <u>simplify</u> the calculation.
❷ <u>Evaluate</u> the power.

● Fractional powers

These are just another way of showing roots. The <u>denominator</u> (bottom) of the fraction <u>tells you which root</u> to take.

> **Examples**
$$5^{\frac{1}{2}} = \sqrt{5}$$
$$8^{\frac{1}{3}} = \sqrt[3]{8}$$

If the <u>numerator</u> (top) is <u>greater than 1</u>, you need to <u>raise the rooted number to this power</u>.

> **Example**
$$8^{\frac{2}{3}} = 8^{\frac{1}{3} \times 2} = \left(8^{\frac{1}{3}}\right)^2 = \left(\sqrt[3]{8}\right)^2 = 2^2 = 4$$

> **Q & A** What is $25^{\frac{3}{2}}$?
Answer
$$25^{\frac{3}{2}} = 25^{\frac{1}{2} \times 3} = \left(25^{\frac{1}{2}}\right)^3$$
$$= \left(\sqrt{25}\right)^3 = 5^3 = \underline{125}$$

> **Method**
❶ Separate the numerator and denominator.
❷ Find the <u>root</u> (given by <u>denominator</u>).
❸ Raise to the <u>power</u> (given by <u>numerator</u>).

1 Find these powers: **a** 4^3 **b** 7^1 **c** 5^{-2} **d** 8^0 **e** 2^5 **f** 16^{-1}

2 Find these roots:
a $\sqrt{36}$ **b** $\sqrt{64}$ **c** $169^{\frac{1}{2}}$ **d** $\sqrt[3]{1000}$ **e** $\sqrt[3]{343}$ **f** $27^{\frac{1}{3}}$

3 Combine these powers: **a** $7^4 \times 7^3$ **b** $2^{10} \div 2^5$ **c** $(5^8)^3$

4 What is $27^{\frac{4}{3}}$?

Check your answers using x^2 x^3 $\sqrt{}$ $\sqrt[3]{}$ x^y on your calculator.

TEST

Rational, irrational & surds (1)

● Rational numbers

Rational numbers are numbers that can be written as fractions (with whole number numerators and denominators). These include whole numbers (both positive and negative), terminating decimals and recurring decimals.

● Irrational numbers

Irrational numbers are non-recurring decimals that go on forever. The most well known irrational number is π (pi).

> ➤ The square roots of non-square whole numbers are irrational.
>
> The cube roots of non-cube whole numbers are irrational.

$\sqrt{5}$ is irrational

$\sqrt{4}$ is rational (= 2)

$\sqrt[3]{24}$ is irrational

● Surds

Surds are expressions with irrational square roots in them, e.g.

$$\sqrt{3} \qquad 5 + \sqrt{6} \qquad 16\sqrt{5} \qquad \frac{12}{\sqrt{3}}$$

● Multiplying & dividing surds

Learn these two important rules.

You must obey these rules.

Two important rules

❶ $\sqrt{a} \times \sqrt{b} = \sqrt{a \times b}$

❷ $\dfrac{\sqrt{a}}{\sqrt{b}} = \sqrt{\dfrac{a}{b}}$

> ➤ $\sqrt{3} \times \sqrt{5} = \sqrt{3 \times 5} = \sqrt{15}$
>
> $\dfrac{\sqrt{12}}{\sqrt{3}} = \sqrt{\dfrac{12}{3}} = \sqrt{4} = 2$

● Adding & subtracting surds

The simple rule is that you cannot add or subtract surds.

$$\sqrt{a} + \sqrt{b} \neq \sqrt{a + b} \qquad\qquad \sqrt{a} - \sqrt{b} \neq \sqrt{a - b}$$

You can only add or subtract surds if they are the same, i.e.

$$\sqrt{3} + 6\sqrt{3} = 7\sqrt{3} \qquad\qquad 10\sqrt{7} - 4\sqrt{7} = 6\sqrt{7}$$

Rational, irrational & surds (2)

● Simplifying surds

Always look for a <u>factor</u> that is a <u>square number</u>, then use '<u>important rule ❶</u>' in reverse ($\sqrt{a \times b} = \sqrt{a} \times \sqrt{b}$).

> **Example**
>
> $\sqrt{150} = \sqrt{25 \times 6} = \sqrt{25} \times \sqrt{6}$
> $\qquad\qquad\qquad\qquad = 5\sqrt{6}$
>
> Square number

● Simplifying fractions with surds in them

You may be asked to '<u>rationalise the denominator</u>' of a fraction with surds in it. This means <u>removing the surds from the denominator</u>.

> **Q & A**
>
> Simplify $\dfrac{4}{7\sqrt{3}}$.
>
> **Answer**
>
> $\dfrac{4}{7\sqrt{3}} = \dfrac{4 \times \sqrt{3}}{7\sqrt{3} \times \sqrt{3}} = \dfrac{4\sqrt{3}}{7\sqrt{3 \times 3}}$
>
> $= \dfrac{4\sqrt{3}}{7\sqrt{9}} = \dfrac{4\sqrt{3}}{7 \times 3} = \dfrac{4\sqrt{3}}{21}$

> **Method**
>
> ❶ Multiply the <u>numerator and denominator</u> by the <u>surd in the denominator</u>.
> ❷ Use '<u>important rule ❶</u>' to tidy it up.

● Classic exam question

> **Q & A**
>
> Simplify $(1 + \sqrt{2})(3 + \sqrt{2})$.
>
> **Answer**
>
> $(1 + \sqrt{2})(3 + \sqrt{2})$
>
> $= (1 \times 3) + (1 \times \sqrt{2}) + (3 \times \sqrt{2}) + (\sqrt{2} \times \sqrt{2})$
>
> $= 3 + \sqrt{2} + 3\sqrt{2} + 2 = 5 + 4\sqrt{2}$

> **Method**
>
> ❶ <u>Multiply out the brackets</u> using the 'face method' on page 32.
> ❷ Use '<u>important rule ❶</u>' to multiply surds together.

---

1 Which of these are rational and which are irrational?

    a $\dfrac{5}{11}$ **b** $\sqrt{7}$ **c** 4π **d** $16\sqrt{4}$ **e** $0.54\dot{2}\dot{3}$ **f** $\sqrt[3]{65}$ **g** $\sqrt[3]{64}$

2 Simplify these:

    a $\dfrac{\sqrt{96}}{\sqrt{6}}$ **b** $\sqrt{180}$ **c** $\dfrac{9}{4\sqrt{5}}$ **d** $(3 + \sqrt{5})(4 - \sqrt{5})$

TEST

BIDMAS & bracket buttons

● BIDMAS

Always do operations in this order:

Brackets, Indices, Divide and Multiply, Add and Subtract

➤ **Q & A**

What is $3 + 2 \times (4 - 1)^2$?

Answer

$3 + 2 \times (4 - 1)^2$

$= 3 + 2 \times 3^2$

$= 3 + 2 \times 9$

$= 3 + 18 = \underline{21}$

➤ **Method**

❶ Do calculations inside brackets first.

❷ Then work out indices, i.e. square, cube, etc.

❸ Divide and multiply.

❹ Finally, add and subtract.

● The bracket buttons (and BIDMAS)

Use the bracket buttons, **( )**, on your calculator to make sure that it works things out in the correct order. Look at this example:

If you want to work out $\frac{34 - 10}{5 + 2}$ you'll get the wrong answer if you press **3 4 − 1 0 ÷ 5 + 2 =**.

This is because calculators use BIDMAS (see above) to work things out. Here a calculator would first work out the division $(10 \div 5)$, then the addition and subtraction.

To get the correct answer you have to use brackets:

(3 4 − 1 0) ÷ (5 + 2) =

● Some other very useful calculator buttons

Make sure you know how to use these important buttons on your calculator.

◀ ▶	These move the curser back and forward along the display.
DEL	It deletes the character where the curser is. Use it with **◀ ▶**.
SHIFT 2nd INV	These let you use functions written above buttons, such as $\tan^{-1}$.

Work these out on paper using BIDMAS. Check your answers using the bracket buttons on your calculator.

a $(3 + 6)(56 - 34)$ **b** $(15 - 2)^2$ **c** $\frac{34 - 24}{6 + 8}$ **d** $\frac{64 \times 44}{128 \div 8}$

TEST

Speedy Revision

Percentages (1)

Make sure you know how to change percentages to fractions and decimals (p12–13).

● Percentage of

➤ Q & A
Find 20% of £400.

Answer

$\frac{20}{100}$ × £400 = £80

or 0.2 × £400 = £80

➤ Method
❶ Write the percentage as a fraction or decimal.
❷ Multiply by the amount given.

● Percentage increase/decrease

➤ Q & A
The price of a game is reduced by 20%. If it cost £30 originally, what is the sale price?

Answer

Decrease = 0.2 × £30 = £6

Sale price = £30 − £6 = £24

➤ Method
❶ Find the decrease (or increase).
❷ Take it off the price. (Add it for an increase.)

Note: Decreasing by 20% is the same as finding 80% so you could do 0.8 × £30 = £24.

● Finding the price before a percentage decrease
Always think of the original price as 100% and work out what percentage the price you're given is. (It will be less than 100%.)

➤ Q & A
In a sale, all items are reduced by 25%.

If a coat costs £37.50 in the sale, how much did it cost originally?

Answer Think of the original price as 100%.
        The cost now is 100% − 25% = 75%.

0.75 × original price = £37.50

So original price = £37.50 ÷ 0.75 = £50

➤ Method
❶ Work out what percentage the price is now.
❷ Write this as a multiplication.
❸ Divide to find the original price.

Percentages (2)

● Finding the price before a percentage increase

You use the <u>same method</u>, but the price now is more than 100%.

➤ Q & A

A bike costs £470 including VAT.

What was the price before VAT was added?

Answer

Think of the price <u>before</u> VAT as 100%.
Price <u>including</u> VAT is 100% + 17.5%
= 117.5% = 1.175.

1.175 × original price = £470

So original price = £470 ÷ 1.175 = <u>£400</u>

➤ Method

❶ Work out <u>what percentage</u> the price is <u>now</u>.

❷ Write this as a <u>multiplication</u>.

❸ <u>Divide</u> to find the <u>original price</u>.

● Percentage change

$$\text{Percentage change} = \frac{\text{Actual change}}{\text{Original quantity}} \times 100\%$$

➤ Q & A

Dave bought a football for £32.
He then sold it for £36.
What was the percentage increase in price?

➤ Method

❶ Write the <u>actual change</u> and <u>original quantity</u>.

❷ Use the <u>formula</u> to work out the <u>percentage change</u>.

Answer

Actual change = £36 − £32 = £4   Original price = £32

So percentage change = $\frac{4}{32} \times 100\%$ = <u>12.5% increase</u>

With money, percentage change is called percentage profit or loss; this was a <u>12.5% profit</u>.

➤ Q & A

A CD player costs £350. In a sale it is reduced to £280.
What is the percentage reduction?

Answer

Actual change = £350 − £280 = £70   Original price = £350

So percentage change = $\frac{70}{350} \times 100\%$ = <u>20% reduction</u>

22

Percentages (3)

● Compound interest

➤ Q & A

£500 was invested for 3 years. Compound interest of 4% was paid annually.

What is the investment now worth?

➤ Method

❶ Work out what you need to multiply by each year.

❷ Multiply to find the total value after 1 year, 2 years...

❸ Stop when you reach the year in question.

Answer

Increasing by 4% is the same as finding 104% so multiply by 1.04.

Year	Start value		End value
1	£500	× 1.04 ➔	£520
2	£520	× 1.04 ➔	£540.80
3	£540.80	× 1.04 ➔	£562.43

Note: You could do this in one step as £500 × 1.04^3 = £562.43.

This one-step method is essential if you are asked to work out something like the interest after 50 years! (See the next Q & A...)

➤ Q & A

How much would the above investment be worth after 50 years?

Answer

£500 × 1.04^{50} = £3553.34

---

1 a What is 15% of 250 g?   b Decrease 250 g by 15%.
2 A jumper is reduced by 10% to £18.
   What was the price before the reduction?
3 The cost including VAT at 17.5% is £94. Take off the VAT.
4 Lauren bought an electronic keyboard for £112, then sold it for £98. What was the percentage loss?
5 A stamp collection was valued at £50 000 three years ago. If stamp prices have risen 12% per year, how much is the collection worth now?
6 £100 is invested at 7% compound interest, paid annually. What is the value of the investment after 20 years?

TEST

Ratio & proportion (1)

● Ratio

In this diagram 1 <u>in every</u> 4 squares is red.

So there is 1 red square <u>for every</u> 3 white squares.

The <u>ratio</u> of red to white squares is <u>1 : 3</u>.

● Simplifying ratios

<u>Multiplying/dividing both sides</u> of a ratio by any number gives an <u>equivalent ratio</u>.

The <u>simplest form</u> has both amounts as <u>whole numbers</u>, with <u>no common factors</u>.

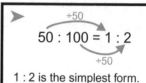

÷50

$50 : 100 = 1 : 2$

÷50

1 : 2 is the simplest form.

● Dividing in a given ratio

➤ Q & A

Divide £120 in the ratio 2 : 3.

Answer

2 + 3 = 5 parts
1 part is £120 ÷ 5 = £24
2 parts are £24 × 2 = <u>£48</u>
3 parts are £24 × 3 = <u>£72</u>
The £120 is split into <u>£48</u> and <u>£72</u>.

➤ Method

❶ Add the ratio to find the <u>total number of parts</u>.
❷ Find the value of <u>1 part</u>.
❸ Multiply by the <u>number of parts</u> on each side of the ratio.

● Increasing or decreasing in a given ratio

Enlargement scale factors are often given as ratios (e.g. on maps).

➤ Q & A

A photograph of height 15 cm is to be increased in the ratio 4 : 3. What is the height of the enlarged photograph?

Answer

❶ 15 cm ÷ 3 = 5 cm

❷ 5 cm × 4 = <u>20 cm</u>

➤ Method (increasing)

❶ <u>Divide</u> by the <u>small number</u> in the ratio.
❷ Then <u>multiply</u> by the <u>large number</u> in the ratio.

For a decrease do the opposite, i.e. <u>divide</u> by the <u>large number</u>, then <u>multiply</u> by the <u>small number</u>.

Always check your answer is sensible. You were asked to <u>increase</u> the height so the answer should be <u>more than 15 cm</u>, which it is.

Ratio & proportion (2)

● Best buy

➤ Q & A

Which of these boxes is better value?

Oats
89p
500 g

Oats
£1.25
750 g

Answer

The small box costs
89 ÷ 500 = 0.178p per gram.

The large box costs
125 ÷ 750 = 0.167p per gram.

As the large box costs less per gram it is better value.

➤ Method

❶ Find the cost per gram by dividing the price by the weight. (Make sure the units are the same.)

❷ The cheapest per gram is the best value.

● Direct proportion

Here you have to first work out the value of one thing.
(These quite often involve recipes.)

➤ Example

If 26 litres cost £19.76,
1 litre costs £19.76 ÷ 26 = £0.76,
so 5 litres cost £0.76 × 5 = £3.80.

See page 60 for more on this topic.

● Inverse proportion

Here as one thing increases (e.g. no. of men) the other decreases (e.g. time taken).

Careful – it's easy to make a mistake.

➤ Example

If it takes 3 men 2 hours to dig a hole,
1 man will take 3 × 2 = 6 hours,
so 2 men will take 6 ÷ 2 = 3 hours.

1 Simplify: **a** 3 : 18 **b** 27 : 15 **c** 1400 : 120

2 Divide 800 ml in the ratio 3 : 7.

3 A photograph has a width of 12 cm.
What is the new width when the photograph is
a enlarged in the ratio 5 : 4 **b** reduced in the ratio 2 : 3?

4 Which of these is better value?
200 g of coffee at £1.79 or 350 g of coffee at £2.79

5 8 notebooks cost £3.60. How much will 15 cost?

6 15 men took 5 hours to build a wall. How long for 20 men?

TEST

Speedy Revision

Rounding & estimating (1)

● Rounding to the nearest 10

➤ The basic method

❶ Find the tens digit.

❷ Look at the next digit to the right (the units!).
If it is <u>5 or more round the tens up</u>.
If it is <u>4 or less leave the tens as they are</u>.

➤ Q & A

Round 8725 to the nearest 10.

Answer

❶ Find the <u>tens digit</u>.   ❷ The number to the <u>right</u> is '<u>5 or more</u>'
so <u>round the tens digit up</u>.

87 2 5 ⫸ 87 3 0

Remember to put a <u>zero as a place holder</u> in the units column.

Rounding to other numbers is similar: 721.6 → 700 to nearest 100,
4846 → 5000 to nearest 1000, 13.52 → 14 to nearest whole number.

● Rounding to decimal places

'<u>Decimal place</u>' is often abbreviated to '<u>dp</u>' or '<u>d.p.</u>'.

When rounding to <u>1 dp</u> find the <u>1st</u> digit after the decimal point.
If the digit to the <u>right is 5 or more</u>, round up. Otherwise round down.
e.g. 3.72 rounds down to 3.7 to 1 dp.

➤ Q & A

Round 0.168 to 2 dp.

Answer

Find the <u>2nd decimal place</u>.

8 is '5 or more',
so round <u>6 up to 7</u>.

0.168 ⫸ 0.17

➤ Method (rounding to 2 dp)

❶ Find the <u>2nd dp</u>.

❷ If the <u>digit to the right</u>
is <u>5 or more</u>, the
<u>2nd dp rounds up</u>.
Otherwise the 2nd dp
stays the same.

Speedy Revision

Rounding & estimating (2)

● Rounding to significant figures

The <u>1st significant figure</u> is the <u>1st non-zero</u> digit from the left.

The 2nd, 3rd, ... significant figures are the digits <u>immediately after</u> the 1st significant figure, even if they are zeros.

> ### ➤ **Example**

1st 2nd 3rd 4th

$$0 . 0 \; 5 \; 0 \; 9 \; 6$$

➤ **Q & A**

Round 5384 to 2 sig figs.

Answer

Find the <u>2nd sig fig</u>.

$$5384 \longrightarrow 5400$$

8 is '5 or more', so round <u>3 up to 4</u>.

Add zeros. (It would be silly to round to 54.)

'<u>Significant figures</u>' is often shortened to '<u>sig figs</u>', '<u>sig. figs.</u>', '<u>sf</u>' or '<u>s.f.</u>'.

> ### ➤ **Method** (rounding to 2 sf)
>
> ❶ Find the <u>2nd sig fig</u>.
> ❷ If the <u>digit to the right</u> of the 2nd sig fig is <u>5 or more</u>, the <u>2nd sig fig rounds up</u>. Otherwise the 2nd sig fig stays the same.

● Estimating calculations

You're bound to be asked to <u>estimate the answer</u> to a calculation on the <u>non-calculator</u> paper. Just <u>round everything</u> to easy numbers (<u>to 1 sig fig</u> usually works quite well).

➤ **Q & A** Estimate the value of $\dfrac{11.6 \times \sqrt{8.8}}{1.8^3 + 7.43}$.

Answer

Rounding all numbers to 1 sig fig gives:
$$\frac{10 \times \sqrt{9}}{2^3 + 7} = \frac{10 \times 3}{8 + 7} = \frac{30}{15} = 2$$

---

1 Round these to 2 decimal places: 0.582, 0.019, 12.882

2 Round these to 2 significant figures: 352, 1.006, 0.809

3 Estimate the answers to these by first rounding all numbers to 1 sf: **a** $\dfrac{5.45 + 10.85}{1.86 + 0.96}$ **b** $\dfrac{989 \times 304}{4.9^2 \times 9.83}$

4 Calculate the exact answer to **3**. Did your estimates give a good approximation?

TEST

Standard index form (1)

● Writing numbers in standard index form

Standard index form (sometimes just called standard form) is a short way of writing really small or large numbers.

A number written in standard form is always 'something times 10 to the power of something':

The first number is always a number between 1 and 10. (It can be 1 but not 10.)

$$3 \times 10^9$$

The power of 10 tells you how far the decimal point has moved.

Written the long way, this number is 3 000 000 000.

➤ Q & A

Write 36 000 in standard form.

Answer

The decimal point needs to move 4 places to get to a number between 1 and 10: 3·6000·

36 000 is greater than 1, so the power of 10 is positive.

So, in standard form, the number is written as 3.6×10^4.

➤ Q & A

Write 0.0045 in standard form.

Answer

The decimal point needs to move 3 places to get to a number between 1 and 10: 0·004·5

0.0045 is less than 1, so the power of 10 is negative.

So, in standard form, the number is written as 4.5×10^{-3}.

➤ Method

❶ Move the decimal point until the number is between 1 and 10.

❷ The power of 10 is the number of places the decimal point moved.

❸ If the original number was greater than 1 then the power is positive.

❹ If the original number was less than 1 then the power is negative.

Write these numbers in standard index form.

a 345

b 0.000 24

c 45 000

d 764 000 000

e 0.000 002 453

f 10 million

TEST

Standard index form (2)

● Changing back to normal numbers

➤ Q & A

Write 2.3×10^{-5} as a normal number.

Answer

The power of 10 is negative so we are dealing with a number less than 1, and the decimal point needs to move 5 places to the left:

Put extra zeros in ➤ $0.00002.3$

So the answer is 0.000 023.

➤ Method

Move the decimal point the number of places indicated by the power of 10.

Remember, negative powers mean that the number is less than 1.

● Multiplying or dividing

➤ Q & A

Work out $(6 \times 10^5) \times (2 \times 10^4)$.

Answer

$(6 \times 10^5) \times (2 \times 10^4)$

$= (6 \times 2) \times (10^5 \times 10^4)$

$= 12 \times 10^{5+4}$

$= 12 \times 10^9$

$= 1.2 \times 10^{10}$

➤ Q & A

Work out $(8 \times 10^7) \div (2 \times 10^3)$.

Answer

$(8 \times 10^7) \div (2 \times 10^3)$

$= (8 \div 2) \times (10^7 \div 10^3)$

$= 4 \times 10^{7-3}$

$= 4 \times 10^4$

➤ Method

❶ Rewrite with the 'numbers between 1 and 10' at the front and the 'powers of 10' together at the end.

❷ Multiply/divide the numbers in the new groups.

❸ Give the answer in standard form (unless asked not to).

See page 17 if you don't know how to multiply or divide powers.

Write these as normal numbers.

a 3.7×10^3 **b** 4.4×10^{-4} **c** 5.43×10^6 **d** 1.2×10^{-6}

TEST

Standard index form (3)

● Adding or subtracting

➤ **Q & A**

Work out $(2.5 \times 10^5) + (3.4 \times 10^4)$.

Answer

$(2.5 \times 10^5) + (3.4 \times 10^4)$

$= 250\,000 + 34\,000$

$= 284\,000$

$= \underline{2.84 \times 10^5}$

➤ **Method**

❶ Change the numbers to normal numbers.

❷ Add or subtract the numbers.

❸ Give the answer in standard form (unless asked not to).

● Standard index form with a calculator

Your calculator will have a button that looks like one of these:

EXP E EE ×10ⁿ . This is the standard form button.

To enter a standard form number like 4.6×10^{11} into your calculator just press **4** ● **6** EXP **1** **1** = and you'll get something

like [4.6 ¹¹   ] on your display (or [4.6×10¹¹   ] if lucky).

➤ **Q & A**

Use your calculator to work out $(4 \times 10^9) + (5 \times 10^{10})$.

Answer

Press **4** EXP **9** **+** **5** EXP **1** **0** =

and you'll get [5.4 ¹⁰   ] or [5.4×10¹⁰   ].

This means the answer is 5.4×10^{10}.

(Do not write 5.4^{10}, that means something else!)

---

1 Give your answers to these in standard index form.

  a $(5 \times 10^5) \times (4 \times 10^4)$ **b** $(4.1 \times 10^3) \times (2 \times 10^4)$

  c $(8 \times 10^9) \div (4 \times 10^6)$ **d** $(1.4 \times 10^{-2}) \div (7 \times 10^{-4})$

  e $(2 \times 10^5) + (4 \times 10^4)$ **f** $(6.4 \times 10^3) + (7 \times 10^4)$

  g $(8 \times 10^{-3}) - (4 \times 10^{-3})$ **h** $(8.2 \times 10^7) - (7 \times 10^5)$

2 Check your answers to **Q1** on your calculator.

TEST

Using letters

● Terms, expressions, equations & formulae

A <u>term</u> is some letters and numbers multiplied (or divided) together, e.g x, $4x$, $8x^2$, $2xy$, 14, $\frac{x}{y}$ and $\frac{x-4}{3}$ are all terms.

An <u>expression</u> is a set of terms added (or subtracted) together, e.g. $4x + 8x^2 - 14$ is an expression.

An <u>equation</u> shows that two expressions are <u>equal</u>, e.g. $x + 2 = 3x$.

A <u>formula</u> is a rule for <u>calculating values</u>, e.g. A can be calculated from B using the formula $A = B + 3$.

Are these terms, expressions, equations or formulae?
a $3ab$ **b** $18c + 19d$ **c** $T = 9p + q$ **d** $x^2 + 4x - 3 = 0$

TEST

Simplifying expressions (1)

● Collecting like terms

'<u>Like terms</u>' are parts of expressions that are similar:

◆ x, $5x$ and $18x$ are like terms (they all have an 'x')
◆ 1, 345, -34 are like terms (they are all just <u>numbers</u>)
◆ xy^2, $14xy^2$, $122xy^2$ are like terms (they all have an 'xy^2')

● Simplifying expressions with brackets

The term in front of a bracket <u>multiplies everything</u> inside it.

➤ Q & A

Expand the brackets and then collect like terms: $5(a + 2b) - 4(a + c)$

Answer

$$5(a + 2b) \qquad -4(a + c)$$

$$= 5 \times a + 5 \times 2b \quad -4 \times a \quad -4 \times c$$

$$= 5a + 10b \qquad -4a \qquad -4c$$

$$= 5a - 4a + 10b - 4c$$

$$= \underline{a + 10b - 4c}$$

➤ Method

❶ <u>Expand</u> brackets. Remember to <u>subtract every term</u> if you are subtracting a bracket.

❷ Combine 'like terms' by <u>adding or subtracting</u> them. (This is often easier if you <u>group</u> 'like terms' together.)

Simplifying expressions (2)

● **Multiplying out double brackets**

➤ **Q & A** Simplify $(2a + 3)(a - 2)$.

Answer

$(2a + 3)(a - 2)$

It doesn't need to be a work of art – just join each term in the first bracket to each term in the second.

$= (2a \times a) + (2a \times -2) + (3 \times a) + (3 \times -2)$

Left eyebrow   Mouth   Nose   Right eyebrow

$= 2a^2 - 4a + 3a - 6$

$= 2a^2 - a - 6$

➤ **Method**

❶ Draw a face with two eyebrows, a nose and a mouth:

❷ Multiply together the terms that are joined by lines.

❸ Collect like terms together.

1 Simplify: **a** $4a + 6a - 4a$ **b** $x^2 + 4x + 2x^2 - 6x + 7x$
  c $7(x - 3y) + 2(x + y)$ **d** $p(5p + 2) - 4(p^2 + p - 1)$

2 Simplify: **a** $(x + 4)(x + 5)$ **b** $(x - 3)(2x + 2)$ **c** $(2y - 6)(2y - 3)$

TEST

Factorising expressions

● **Factorising**

Factorising means putting brackets in.

➤ **Q & A** Factorise $20x^2 - 15x$.

Answer

$20x^2 - 15x$

$= 5(4x^2 - 3x)$ 5 is a factor, so take it out.

$= 5x(4x - 3)$ x is also a factor, so take it out too.

Not sure what a factor is? It's something that divides exactly into all the terms.

➤ **Method**

❶ Look for a common factor. Take this outside the bracket.

❷ Look again. If you can see another factor take it outside the bracket too.

❸ Repeat until no factors are left.

1 Factorise: **a** $6y - 2$ **b** $rs + r$ **c** $18y^2 - 4y$ **d** $12r^2s + 3rs - 4s$

2 Simplify this fraction by first factorising the numerator and denominator, then cancelling. $\dfrac{5x^2 - 20x}{x^3 - 4x^2}$

TEST

See page 49 for how to factorise trickier quadratics.

Speedy Revision

Formulae

● Writing a formula

➤ Q & A

A plumber charges £20 to come out, plus £15 for every hour worked. Write a formula for the total cost, C, for a job taking t hours.

Answer

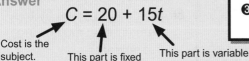

$$C = 20 + 15t$$

Cost is the subject.

This part is fixed – you always have to pay £20.

This part is variable – it depends how long the job takes.

➤ Method

❶ Write down '<u>subject =</u>'. (The subject is the thing the formula will be used to calculate.)

❷ Start the formula with the <u>fixed</u> part.

❸ Finish with the <u>variable</u> part.

● Putting numbers into a formula

Often called <u>substituting values</u> or just plain <u>substitution</u>.

➤ Q & A

Find the value of $v = u + at$ when $u = 4$, $a = -3$ and $t = 5$.

Answer

$v = u + at$

$v = 4 + -3 \times 5$

$v = 4 + -15$

$v = 4 - 15$

$v = -11$

Do BIDMAS a step at a time, just in case you make a mistake.

➤ Method

❶ Write out the <u>formula</u>.

❷ Write it out again with the <u>numbers in place of the letters</u>.

❸ Use <u>BIDMAS</u> (p20) to calculate the value.

---

1 Al buys p pens costing £1.50 each. He pays with a £10 note. Write a formula for the amount of change (C) he receives.

2 What is the cost of hiring a plumber for 20 hours? ($C = 20 + 15t$)

3 Find the value of $v = u + at$ when:
   a $u = 7$, $a = 2$, $t = 3$ **b** $u = 0$, $a = -2$, $t = 8$

4 Given that $x = 3$, find the value of y when:
   a $y = 3x^2 + 4$ **b** $y = 2x^3$

TEST

Rearranging formulae

Making x the subject of a formula means rewriting it as $x = ...$

● What to do with powers of the subject

➤ Q & A

Make x the subject of $y = 36x^2$.

Answer

$y = 36x^2$

$\sqrt{y} = 6x$ [square root]

$\dfrac{\sqrt{y}}{6} = x$ [÷6]

$x = \dfrac{\sqrt{y}}{6}$ [rewrite]

➤ Method
❶ If the subject has been squared, square root both sides of the equation. If the subject has been cubed, take the cube root.
❷ Divide both sides by the number now multiplying the subject.
❸ Rewrite the equation with the subject on the left.

● What to do if the subject occurs twice

➤ Q & A

Make x the subject of $x + 6 = xy + y$.

Answer

$x + 6 = xy + y$

$x + 6 - xy = y$ [−xy]

$x - xy = y - 6$ [−6]

$x(1 - y) = y - 6$ [factorise]

$x = \dfrac{y - 6}{1 - y}$ [÷(1 − y)]

➤ Method
❶ Collect all terms containing the subject on the left side.
❷ Collect all other terms (i.e. ones without the subject in) on the right.
❸ Factorise the left side by taking out the subject.
❹ Divide both sides by the expression that is now multiplying the subject.

If you're asked to make x the subject of a formula like $y = \dfrac{x - 4}{x + 5}$ you'll need to first multiply by the denominator, $x + 5$.
After multiplying out (giving $xy + 5y = x - 4$) you can follow the method above.

---

1 Make q the subject of   **a** $p = 4q^2$ **b** $p = 81q^2$

2 Make a the subject of   **a** $2a + 3b = a + 1$ **b** $b = \dfrac{a - 4}{a + 5}$

TEST

34

Speedy Revision

Solving equations

● Solving linear equations without brackets

Remember: Whatever you do to one side you must do to the other.

➤ Q & A (1)

Solve $7x - 4 = x + 2$.

Answer

$7x - 4 = x + 2$

$6x - 4 = 2$ [$-x$]

$6x = 6$ [$+4$]

$x = 1$ [$\div 6$]

➤ Method

❶ Get rid of the <u>smallest x-term</u>. x is now on one side only.

❷ <u>Add/subtract</u> any <u>numbers</u> on the x-side to/from both sides.

❸ <u>Divide both sides</u> by the number multiplying x.

● Equations with brackets and fractions

➤ Q & A (2)

Solve $6(3y - 2) = 3(3y + 5)$.

Answer

$6 \times 3y - 6 \times 2 = 3 \times 3y + 3 \times 5$ [expand brackets]

$18y - 12 = 9y + 15$

You can now solve this using the first method (see TEST Q2).

➤ Method

❶ <u>Expand</u> the <u>brackets</u>.

❷ Solve as above.

➤ Q & A (3)

Solve $\dfrac{p - 3}{2} = \dfrac{2p + 1}{3}$.

Answer

$\dfrac{p - 3}{2} \times 6 = \dfrac{2p + 1}{3} \times 6$ [$\times 6$]

$3(p - 3) = 2(2p + 1)$

$3p - 9 = 4p + 2$ [expand brackets]

You can now solve this using the first method (see TEST Q3).

➤ Method

❶ <u>Multiply both sides</u> by the <u>LCM</u> of the <u>denominators</u>.

❷ <u>Expand</u> the <u>brackets</u>.

❸ Solve as above.

---

1 Solve $5g + 3 = 2g + 6$.   **2** Finish **Q & A (2)**.

3 Finish **Q & A (3)**.

4 Solve: **a** $2(13 - m) = m + 2$ **b** $\dfrac{n}{2} = \dfrac{n + 4}{4}$

TEST

Trial & improvement

● Solving equations

<u>Essential</u>: you must show all your working.

➤ Q & A

The equation $x^3 + x = 75$ has a solution between 4 and 5. Use trial and improvement to find the solution to 2 d.p.

Answer

➤ Method

❶ Make a <u>sensible guess</u> for x and substitute it into the equation (use a calculator!).

❷ If the left-hand side is <u>too big/small</u>, take a <u>smaller/ bigger guess</u>.

❸ Stop when you have two numbers that bound x and <u>round to the same number</u>.

x	$x^3 + x$		
4.5	95.625	too big	x is between 4 and 4.5
4.2	78.288	too big	x is between 4 and 4.2
4.1	73.021	too small	x is between 4.1 and 4.2
4.15	75.623375	too big	x is between 4.1 and 4.15
4.13	74.574997	too small	x is between 4.13 and 4.15
4.14	75.097944	too big	x is between 4.13 and 4.14

To see if the solution is 4.13 or 4.14 you need to try the <u>mid-value</u>:

4.135	74.83616...	too small	x is between 4.135 and 4.14

4.135 & 4.14 both round to 4.14, so the solution is <u>$x = 4.14$</u> to 2 d.p.

The last step in the **Q & A** can be seen clearly on a number line:

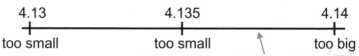

The solution must be in here.

● Finding roots

You can find values of roots, such as $\sqrt[3]{12}$, by trial and improvement. You start by taking a guess at the root. In the case of $\sqrt[3]{12}$, your first guess could be 2. Cubing this gives 8, which is smaller than 12 so your next guess needs to be bigger.

1 Find the solution of $x^3 - x = 50$ correct to 2 decimal places.
2 Find the value of $\sqrt[3]{12}$ correct to 1 decimal place.

TEST

Speedy Revision

Coordinates

● 3-D coordinates

Coordinates in <u>3-D</u> have <u>3 parts</u>: (x, y, z)

➤ ABCDEFGH is a cuboid.
   Vertex C has coordinates (4, 3, 2).

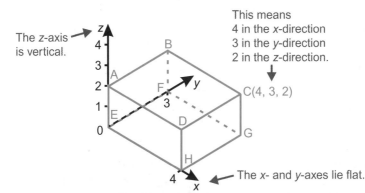

The z-axis is vertical.

This means
4 in the x-direction
3 in the y-direction
2 in the z-direction.

C(4, 3, 2)

The x- and y-axes lie flat.

● The midpoint of a line between two points

➤ Q & A

Find the midpoint of the line between A(2, 1) and B(4, 3).

Answer

❶ The mean of the x-coordinates
   = (2 + 4) ÷ 2 = <u>3</u>
❷ The mean of the y-coordinates
   = (1 + 3) ÷ 2 = <u>2</u>
❸ The midpoint is at <u>(3, 2)</u>.

Check your answer
by sketching a graph.

➤ Method

❶ Find the <u>average</u> (mean) of the <u>x-coordinates</u>.
❷ Find the <u>average</u> (mean) of the <u>y-coordinates</u>.
❸ These are the <u>coordinates</u> of the <u>midpoint</u>.

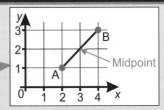

If the coordinates are in 3-D you also need to find the mean of the z-coordinates.

1 Write down the coordinates of points A to H in the example.
2 Find the midpoint of the line between P(6, 3) and Q(2, 9).

TEST

Straight-line graphs (1)

● Plotting and drawing straight-line graphs

The secret to drawing graphs is to first construct a <u>table of values</u>.

➤ Q & A

Complete this table of values
for the equation $y = 2x + 2$ and
then draw its graph.

x	−2	−1	0	1	2
$y = 2x + 2$		0		4	

Answer

The missing values are when $x = −2$, $x = 0$ and $x = 2$.
Putting these values into the equation gives:

when $x = −2$: $y = 2x + 2 = 2 \times (−2) + 2 = −4 + 2 = \underline{−2}$
when $x = 0$: $y = 2x + 2 = 2 \times 0 + 2 = 0 + 2 = \underline{2}$
when $x = 2$: $y = 2x + 2 = 2 \times 2 + 2 = 4 + 2 = \underline{6}$

So the completed table is:

x	−2	−1	0	1	2
$y = 2x + 2$	−2	0	2	4	6

Next plot the points one at a
time on graph paper:

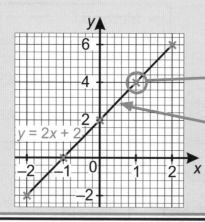

This pair of values
gives the point (1, 4).

(1, 4) is plotted here.

Finally, use a <u>ruler</u> to
draw a straight line
through the points.

---

a Copy and complete the
table of values for the
equation $y = 3x + 2$.

x	−2	−1	0	1	2
$y = 3x + 2$	−4			5	

b Draw the graph of $y = 3x + 2$ on graph paper.
(The x-axis should go from −2 to 2 and the y-axis should go from −4 to 8.)

TEST

Straight-line graphs (2)

● What to do when *x* and *y* are on the same side

You might well be asked to draw the graph of $3x + 4y = 12$.

You could rearrange the equation so that *y* is on the left on its own (i.e. $y = -\frac{3}{4}x + 3$) and then draw a table of values.

The other, quicker, way is to:

❶ Put $x = 0$ in the equation and then find *y*; this is where the graph crosses the *y*-axis. In $3x + 4y = 12$ when $x = 0$, $4y = 12$, i.e. $y = 3$.

❷ Put $y = 0$ in the equation and then find *x*; this is where the graph crosses the *x*-axis. In $3x + 4y = 12$ when $y = 0$, $3x = 12$, i.e. $x = 4$.

❸ Plot these two points and join them with a straight line.
For $3x + 4y = 12$, you need to plot (0, 3) and (4, 0).

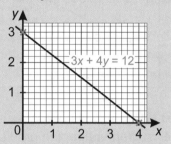

● Gradient

The gradient of a line indicates how steep it is. Use this formula to work them out:

$$\text{Gradient} = \frac{\text{vertical change}}{\text{horizontal change}}$$
$$= \frac{\text{change in } y}{\text{change in } x}$$

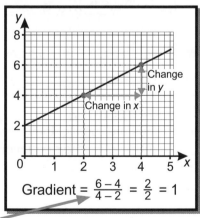

$$\text{Gradient} = \frac{6-4}{4-2} = \frac{2}{2} = 1$$

Just pick two points on the line, then divide the vertical change by the horizontal change.

● Positive or negative gradient?

If the graph slopes upwards (╱) the gradient will be positive.

If the graph slopes downwards (╲) the gradient will be negative.

Straight-line graphs (3)

● *y = mx + c*

m is the <u>gradient</u>. The greater the value of *m* the <u>steeper</u> the graph.

c is the <u>y-intercept</u>. This tells you the graph cuts the y-axis at <u>(0, c)</u>.

➤ Q & A

Find the equation of this straight line.

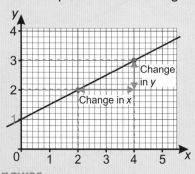

➤ Method

❶ Work out <u>m</u> (the <u>gradient</u>).

❷ Find <u>c</u> (where the line <u>cuts the y-axis</u>).

❸ Pop the values of <u>m</u> and <u>c</u> into the equation <u>y = mx + c</u>.

Answer

❶ First work out <u>m</u>, the gradient.

$$m = \frac{\text{change in } y}{\text{change in } x} = \frac{3-2}{4-2} = \frac{1}{2}$$

⬅ The gradient is <u>positive</u> as the line slopes <u>upwards</u>.

❷ The graph cuts the y-axis at (0, <u>1</u>), so <u>c = 1</u>.

❸ This gives the equation $y = \frac{1}{2}x + 1$.

● Parallel lines

If two lines are <u>parallel</u> they have the <u>same gradient</u>, so their equations will have the <u>same value of m</u>.

For example

$y = \underline{2}x + 3$
$y = \underline{2}x + 1$
$y = \underline{2}x - 2$

all have gradient <u>2</u>, so they are parallel.

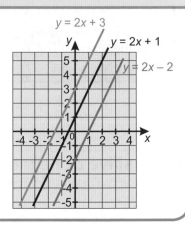

40

Straight-line graphs (4)

● Perpendicular lines

If two lines are <u>perpendicular</u> then the <u>product of their gradients is −1</u>.

For example, $y = 2x + 3$ and $y = -\frac{1}{2}x - 1$ are perpendicular because $2 \times -\frac{1}{2} = \underline{-1}$.

The lines meet at <u>right angles</u>.

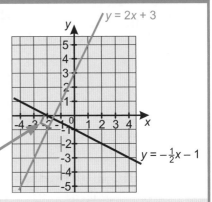

$y = 2x + 3$

$y = -\frac{1}{2}x - 1$

➤ Q & A

What is the equation of the line that goes through the point (0, 4) and is perpendicular to $y = -\frac{1}{3}x + 1$?

Answer

Let the gradient of the perpendicular line be m, then

$$m \times -\frac{1}{3} = -1, \text{ so } \underline{m = 3}$$

The line goes through (0, 4), so $\underline{c = 4}$.

Putting $m = 3$ and $c = 4$ into $y = mx + c$ gives $\underline{y = 3x + 4}$.

➤ Method

❶ <u>Find m</u>, using the fact that the product of the gradients of perpendicular lines is −1.

❷ <u>Find c</u> (y-intercept).

❸ Put the values of $\underline{m}$ and $\underline{c}$ into $\underline{y = mx + c}$.

1 By first constructing a table of values from $x = -2$ to $x = 3$, plot the graph of $y = 3x - 4$.

2 State the gradient of each line and where it crosses the y-axis.
   a $y = 3x + 5$ b $y = 2x - 1$

3 Find the equation of the line that goes through the point (0, −2) and is
   a parallel to $y = -4x + 1$
   b perpendicular to $y = -4x + 1$.

4 Work out the equations of the lines below.

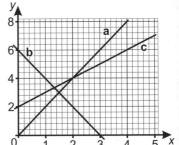

TEST

Inequalities (1)

➤ Q & A

List all the integer values of
n that satisfy $-2 \leqslant n < 3$.

Answer

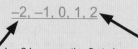
$-2, -1, 0, 1, 2$

Include -2 because the first sign
means greater than or <u>equal to -2</u>.

Stop at 2 because the second
sign means <u>less than 3</u>.

The four inequality symbols

< means '<u>less than</u>'.

⩽ means '<u>less than or equal to</u>'.

> means '<u>greater than</u>'.

⩾ means '<u>greater than or equal to</u>'.

● Solving an inequality

You solve inequalities in <u>exactly</u> the same way as equations, with
one exception: if you <u>multiply or divide by a negative number</u> you
must <u>reverse the inequality</u> symbol.

For example, $-3x > 6$ becomes $x < -2$ when you divide by -3.

➤ Q & A

Solve $7x < 8x + 3$.

Answer

This is just like solving
equations – see page 35.

$$7x < 8x + 3$$
$$0 < x + 3 \qquad \text{[}-7x \text{ from \underline{both} sides]}$$
$$-3 < x \qquad \text{[}-3 \text{ from \underline{both} sides]}$$
$$x > -3 \qquad \text{[rewrite with } x \text{ on the left]}$$

-3 is less than x,
so x is more than -3.

● Showing inequalities on a number line

➤ Q & A

Show $x < -2$ and $0 \leqslant x < 5$ on a
number line.

Answer

<u>Shade</u> this circle because the inequality
was '⩽', so <u>0 is included</u>.

○ means <u>not included</u>

● means <u>is included</u>

Use arrows to show more
numbers are included.

$x < -2$　　　　$0 \leqslant x < 5$

```
◄──────────○────●───────────○──────►
 -6 -5 -4 -3 -2 -1  0  1  2  3  4  5  6
```

<u>Do not shade</u> as the inequality
was '<', so <u>5 is not included</u>.

<u>Do not shade</u> this circle as the inequality was '<', so <u>-2 is not included</u>.

Speedy Revision

Inequalities (2)

● Showing inequalities on a graph

➤ Q & A

Shade the region on a graph that satisfies $y < x$ and $x \leq 5$.

Answer

First, plot the lines $y = x$ and $x = 5$.

Broken lines show points are not included (use if inequality was '<' or '>').

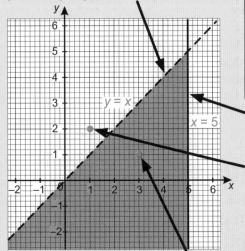

➤ Method

❶ Replace the inequality symbols with '='.

❷ Draw the lines (plot a table of values or use $y = mx + c$).

❸ Pick a point (not on a line) and if it satisfies the original inequalities shade this region. If not try another point in a different region.

Solid lines show points are included (use for '$\leq$' and '$\geq$').

Pick a point, e.g. (1, 2), and see if it fits the inequalities:

$2 < 1$ and $2 \leq 5$ ✗

(1, 2) does not satisfy $y < x$.

So, pick another point, e.g. (3, 1), and see if it fits the inequalities:

$1 < 3$ and $3 \leq 5$ ✓   (3, 1) works, so shade the region it's in.

---

1 **a** List integer values of n that satisfy $-5 < n \leq 1$.

  b Show $-5 < n \leq 1$ on a number line.

2 **a** Solve $2x + 2 < x + 4$.

  b Show the solution on a number line.

3 Shade the region on a graph that satisfies $y > -2$ and $y \leq 2x$.

4 **a** Solve $10y - 5 \leq 6y + 3$.

  b Show the solution on a graph.

TEST

Equation of a circle

The equation of a circle <u>centred on the origin</u> with <u>radius r</u> is:

$$x^2 + y^2 = r^2$$

● Drawing a circle from its equation

➤ Q & A

Draw the graph of $2y^2 = -2x^2 + 8$.

If there's an x^2 and a y^2 it's probably a circle.

Answer

> ### ➤ Method
> ❶ Write the equation in the form $x^2 + y^2 = r^2$.
> ❷ Use your <u>compasses</u> to draw a circle <u>centred on the origin</u> with <u>radius r</u>.

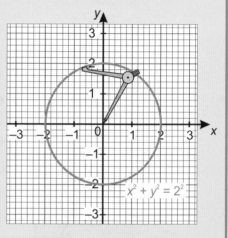

$2y^2 + 2x^2 = 8$	$[+2x^2]$
$y^2 + x^2 = 4$	$[\div 2]$
$x^2 + y^2 = 2^2$	

So the radius, r, is 2 units.

● Finding the equation of a circle from its graph

Just write down where the circle <u>cuts the positive x- or y-axis</u>. This is the <u>radius r</u>.

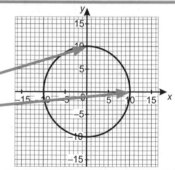

Here r is 10.
So the equation is $x^2 + y^2 = 10^2$
or $x^2 + y^2 = 100$

---

1 Draw the graphs of these equations:
  a $y^2 + x^2 = 400$
  b $y^2 = -x^2 + 81$
  c $x^2 + 2x + 4 = -y^2 + 2x + 20$

2 What is the equation of this circle?

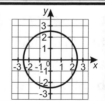

TEST

44

Simultaneous equations (1)

● Solving simultaneous equations graphically

You'll be given two equations. These could be:

◆ two linear equations (i.e. two straight lines)
◆ a straight line and a quadratic
◆ or a straight line and a circle.

The basic method is the same for all three cases:

> You just have to draw the graphs of the two equations.
> The point(s) where they cross gives the solution(s).

● Two straight lines (linear equations)

➤ Q & A

Solve graphically:

$y = x + 2$

$y = 4 - x$

Answer

➤ Method

❶ Draw a table of values.
❷ Plot the graphs.
❸ Read off the x- and y-values where the graphs cross.

You only need two points to draw a straight line, but plot three in case you make a mistake.

x	−2	0	2
$y = x + 2$	0	2	4
$y = 4 - x$	6	4	2

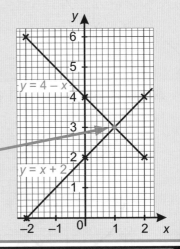

The graphs cross at (1, 3) so the solution is:

$x = 1$ and $y = 3$

---

1 Solve graphically:

$y = x - 3$

$y = 9 - 2x$

2 Solve graphically:

$y = -x$

$y = 3x - 4$

3 Why do $y = 2x + 3$ and $y = 2x - 1$ have no solution?

TEST

Simultaneous equations (2)

● A straight line and a quadratic

➤ Q & A

Solve graphically:
$y = x^2 + x - 2$
$y = 2x + 2$

Answer

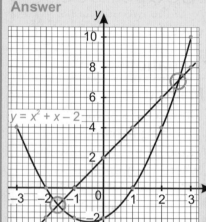

➤ Method

❶ <u>Plot</u> the graphs of the equations. Use a <u>table of values</u> for both the <u>linear</u> and <u>quadratic</u> equations.

❷ Read off the <u>x- and y-values</u> where the graphs <u>cross</u>.

The first equation is a <u>quadratic</u> and the second is <u>linear</u> so draw a <u>table of values</u>.

x	−3	−2	−1	0	1	2	3
$y = x^2 + x - 2$	4	0	−2	−2	0	4	10
$y = 2x + 2$	−4	−2	0	2	4	6	8

The graphs cross at (−1.6, −1.2) and (2.6, 7.2) so there are two solutions:
<u>$x = -1.6$, $y = -1.2$ or $x = 2.6$, $y = 7.2$</u>

● A straight line and a circle

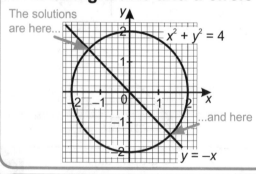

The solutions are here...
$x^2 + y^2 = 4$
...and here
$y = -x$

➤ Method

❶ <u>Plot</u> the graphs of the equations. Use $x^2 + y^2 = r^2$ for the circle (see page 44).

❷ Read off the <u>x- and y-values</u> where the graphs <u>cross</u>.

Solve these graphically:
a $y^2 = -x^2 + 25$
   $y = 3x - 4$

b $y - x^2 = 2x + 4$
   $y = 3 - x$

TEST

Simultaneous equations (3)

● **Solving simultaneous equations algebraically**

You don't have to draw a graph to solve simultaneous equations – you can solve them algebraically. Just remember that you're looking for values of the two variables that work in both equations.

● **Two linear equations**

➤ **Q & A**

Solve algebraically:

$y = 6x - 16$

$2x + 3y = 12$

Answer

A $\quad -6x + y = -16 \quad$ [$-6x$]

B $\quad 2x + 3y = 12 \quad$ [OK]

C $\quad -6x + y = -16$

D $\quad \underline{6x + 9y = 36} \quad$ [×3]

$\qquad 10y = 20 \quad$ [C + D]

$\qquad y = 2 \quad$ [÷10]

➤ **Method**

❶ Rewrite both equations as $ax + by = c$. Label **A** and **B**.

❷ Multiply one (or both) of the equations by something to get the same number in front of x (or y) in both equations. Label **C** and **D**.

❸ Add/subtract one equation to/from the other to eliminate x or y.

❹ Solve this equation.

❺ Substitute this value into one of the original equations.

❻ Solve this equation.

$2x + 6 = 12 \quad$ [put $y = 2$ into **B**]

$\qquad 2x = 6 \quad$ [−6]

$\qquad x = 3 \quad$ [÷2] $\qquad$ So the solution is $x = 3$ and $y = 2$.

Check the answer by putting the $x = 3$ and $y = 2$ back into the original equations:

❼ Check your answer.

$y = 6x - 16 \ \Longrightarrow\ (6 × 3) - 16 = 2 \ ✓$

$2x + 3y = 12 \ \Longrightarrow\ (2 × 3) + (3 × 2) = 12 \ ✓$

1 Solve algebraically:

$4x - 3y = 8$

$x + y = 9$

2 Solve algebraically:

$y = 2x + 6$

$3y - x = 8$

TEST

Simultaneous equations (4)

● One of the equations is a quadratic or a circle

➤ Q & A

Solve algebraically:

$y^2 + x^2 = 20$

$-x + y = 2$

Answer

$-x + y = 2$ becomes $y = x + 2$.

Substitute this into $y^2 + x^2 = 20$

to get:

$(x + 2)^2 + x^2 = 20$

$x^2 + 4x + 4 + x^2 = 20$

$2x^2 + 4x - 16 = 0$

$x^2 + 2x - 8 = 0$

$(x + 4)(x - 2) = 0$

So $x = -4$ or $x = 2$

➤ Method

❶ Rewrite the <u>linear equation</u> as '$y =$' (if necessary).

❷ <u>Substitute</u> the 'y' from ❶ into the <u>other equation</u>.

❸ <u>Solve</u> the new equation to find 'x'. (This may involve solving a quadratic.)

❹ <u>Substitute</u> the value(s) of x back into the <u>linear equation</u> to find the corresponding value(s) of y.

❺ <u>Check</u> your answer.

Putting these values of x back into $y = x + 2$ gives two solutions: <u>$x = -4, y = -2$ or $x = 2, y = 4$</u>.

Check your answer by putting the solutions back into $y^2 + x^2 = 20$:

When $x = -4$ and $y = -2$, $y^2 + x^2 = (-2)^2 + (-4)^2 = 4 + 16 = 20$ ✓

When $x = 2$ and $y = 4$, $y^2 + x^2 = 4^2 + 2^2 = 16 + 4 = 20$ ✓

● There's no excuse for getting it wrong!

As you can see from the **Q & A** above, you should get these right every time, because you can <u>check your answer</u>. In fact any time you've solved equations you should check your solutions by popping them back into the <u>original equations</u>.

TEST

1 Solve these algebraically:

    a $y = 3x - 3$ **b** $y^2 = -x^2 + 25$ **c** $y - 2x^2 = 4x + 2$

       $y = 9 - 2x$ $2y = 2x - 2$ $y - 3x = 3$

2 Why do $y^2 + x^2 = 16$ and $y = -5$ have no solution?

48

Quadratics (1)

All quadratic equations (in x) can be written as $ax^2 + bx + c = 0$.

● Factorising quadratics when 'a' is 1

> ### Q & A
Factorise $x^2 + 3x - 10$.

Answer

$x^2 + 3x - 10 = (x + ?)(x + ?)$

Factor pairs for –10 are:

$1 \times -10, -1 \times 10, 2 \times -5$ and -2×5

Only $-2 + 5 = 3$, so:

$x^2 + 3x - 10 = (x + -2)(x + 5)$

$\qquad = \underline{(x - 2)(x + 5)}$ ◄─ Check this by multiplying out. Go on!

> ### Method
❶ Write out the brackets.
❷ Note down <u>factor pairs</u> of the <u>constant</u>.
❸ Choose the ones that <u>add together</u> to give the number in front of x.
❹ <u>Always</u> multiply out to check your answer.

● Factorising quadratics when 'a' is <u>not</u> 1

Basically, start by looking for two numbers that have a product of <u>ac</u> and a sum of <u>b</u>.

> ### Q & A
Factorise $3x^2 - 5x - 2$.

Answer

Here $a = 3$, $b = -5$, $c = -2$
So $ac = 3 \times (-2) = -6$

Factor pairs for –6 are:
$1 \times -6, -1 \times 6, 2 \times -3$ and -2×3

Only $1 + -6 = -5$, so:
$3x^2 - 5x - 2 = 3x^2 + x + -6x - 2$
$\qquad = x(3x + 1) - 2(3x + 1)$
$\qquad = \underline{(3x + 1)(x - 2)}$

Check this by multiplying out. Yes, you!

> ### Method
❶ Write as $ax^2 + bx + c$ (if necessary).
❷ Write down all the <u>factor pairs</u> of ac.
❸ Pick out the pair from ❷ that add to make <u>b</u>.
❹ Rewrite the <u>bx term</u> using this pair.
❺ Factorise the <u>first two terms</u>, then factorise the <u>second two terms</u>.
❻ Combine the brackets.
❼ <u>Always</u> multiply out to check your answer.

Note: If you use a different method (and can do these error free) then great.
If not, learn this method – and practise, practise, practise, ...

Quadratics (2)

● 'Difference of two squares'

Quadratics of the form $x^2 - a^2$ always factorise as $(x + a)(x - a)$.

➤ **Examples**

$x^2 - 1 = (x + 1)(x - 1)$

$4x^2 - 9 = (2x + 3)(2x - 3)$

● Solving quadratic equations by factorising

This relies on the fact that if $p \times q = 0$ then either $p = 0$ or $q = 0$.

➤ **Q & A**

Solve $x^2 + 3x = 10$.

Answer

$x^2 + 3x - 10 = 0$ [−10]

So $(x - 2)(x + 5) = 0$ [page 49]

$x - 2 = 0$ gives $\underline{x = 2}$

$x + 5 = 0$ gives $\underline{x = -5}$

So the solutions are $\underline{x = 2 \text{ or } x = -5}$.

➤ **Method**

❶ Move all terms to the left so '= 0' is on the right.

❷ Factorise the quadratic expression.

❸ Put one of the brackets equal to zero and solve.

❹ Repeat for the other bracket.

> Tip: Always try to take out a common factor.

For example, if faced with $10x^2 - 5x - 75 = 0$, you should spot that each term has a common factor of 5, so take it out to get

$$5(2x^2 - x - 15) = 0.$$

Then factorise the quadratic expression in the bracket:

$$5(2x + 5)(x - 3) = 0.$$

(This gives the solutions of $x = -\frac{5}{2}$ or $x = 3$.)

---

1 Factorise   **a** $x^2 + 7x + 6$ **b** $x^2 - 11x + 10$ **c** $x^2 - 2x - 15$

2 Factorise   **a** $2x^2 - 9x + 4$ **b** $6x^2 + 10x + 4$ **c** $4x^2 + 7x - 15$

3 Factorise   **a** $x^2 - 36$ **b** $9x^2 - 49$ **c** $4p^2 - 16q^2$

4 Solve these equations.

    a $x^2 - 5x + 4 = 0$ **b** $x^2 - 16 = 0$ **c** $x^2 + 5x + 6 = 0$

    d $25x^2 - 100 = 0$ **e** $5x^2 + 3 = 16x$ **f** $2x^2 + 14x + 24 = 0$

TEST

Quadratics (3)

If you can't factorise the equation use one of these two methods.

● **The quadratic formula** (sometimes just called 'the formula')

The two solutions to the quadratic equation $ax^2 + bx + c = 0$ are given by the quadratic formula:

$$x = \frac{-b \pm \sqrt{b^2 - 4ac}}{2a}$$

➤ Q & A

Use the quadratic formula to solve $4x^2 + 6x - 5 = 0$ to 1 dp.

Answer

$a = 4, b = 6, c = -5$

So $x = \dfrac{-6 \pm \sqrt{6^2 - (4 \times 4 \times -5)}}{2 \times 4}$

$x = \dfrac{-6 \pm \sqrt{116}}{8} = \dfrac{-6 \pm 10.77}{8} = \underline{0.6 \text{ or } -2.1}$

➤ Method

❶ Write the equation in the form $ax^2 + bx + c = 0$.

❷ Put the values of <u>a, b, and c</u> into the <u>quadratic formula</u>.

❸ Calculate the <u>2 solutions</u>.

If you think you've messed up, you can check your answer by putting the values back into the original equation.

● **Completing the square**

➤ Q & A

By first completing the square, solve $x^2 - 2x - 4 = 0$. Leave your answer in surd form.

Answer

$x^2 - 2x - 4 = 0$

Now $(x - 1)^2 = x^2 - 2x + 1$

need to subtract 5 to get -4

So $(x - 1)^2 - 5 = 0$

$(x - 1)^2 = 5$

Taking square roots gives

$x - 1 = \pm\sqrt{5}$. So $\underline{x = 1 + \sqrt{5} \text{ or } x = 1 - \sqrt{5}}$.

➤ Method

❶ Write the equation in the form $x^2 + bx + c = 0$.

❷ Write the bracket $(x + \frac{b}{2})^2$.

❸ <u>Expand</u> to see what you need to <u>add/subtract</u> to get the original equation.

❹ Move the constant to the rhs.

❺ Take the <u>square root</u> (positive <u>and</u> negative).

❻ Work out the <u>2 solutions</u>.

Solve these to 1 dp by completing the square.
a $2x^2 + 6x - 4 = 0$ **b** $3x^2 - 27x - 2 = 7$
Check your answers by using the quadratic formula.

TEST

Quadratics (4)

● Quadratic graphs

A quadratic graph is always:

∪-shaped if the number multiplying x^2 is positive

∩-shaped if the number multiplying x^2 is negative.

➤ Q & A

Draw the graph of $y = x^2 + x - 3$.

Answer

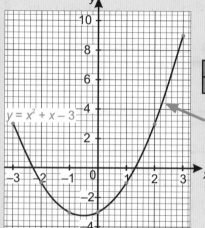

➤ Method

❶ Draw a table of values.
❷ Plot the points.
❸ Join the points with a smooth curve.

First draw a table of values:

x	−3	−2	−1	0	1	2	3
$y = x^2 + x - 3$	3	−1	−3	−3	−1	3	9

Draw a smooth curve. Do not draw straight lines between the points.

The graph is ∪-shaped because there is no minus sign in front of x^2.

● Using graphs to solve quadratic equations

To solve $ax^2 + bx + c = 0$, plot $y = ax^2 + bx + c$ and see where $y = 0$ (i.e. where the graph cuts the x-axis).

➤ Q & A

Use the graph above to solve $x^2 + x - 3 = 0$.

Answer

$y = 0$ when $x = -2.3$ and when $x = 1.3$.

By first plotting $y = x^2 - x - 4$, solve $x^2 - x - 4 = 0$.
(Draw your x-axis from −3 to 3 and your y-axis from −6 to 10.)

TEST

Speedy Revision

Quadratics (5)

Drawing the graph of a quadratic is the easy bit!
Make sure you can do these <u>nasty follow-up questions</u>.

➤ Q & A

Using the graph of $y = x^2 + x - 3$
(page 52), solve $x^2 - x - 1 = 0$.

Answer

$x^2 - x - 1 = 0$

$x^2 + x - 3 = 2x - 2$ [+2x, −2]

You've drawn this side,   Now draw
i.e. $y = x^2 + x - 3$. $y = 2x - 2$.

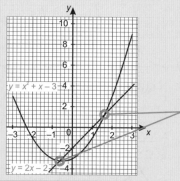

➤ Method

❶ <u>Rearrange</u> the equation
you want to solve so that
the <u>left side</u> is the same
as the <u>equation of the
graph you have drawn</u>.

❷ <u>Draw the line</u> given by the
<u>expression on the right</u>
(it's always a line).

❸ The points where the <u>line
and curve meet</u> are the
<u>solutions</u>.

The graphs cross at $x = -0.6$
and $x = 1.6$, so these are the
solutions to $x^2 + x - 3 = 2x - 2$.

So the solutions to $x^2 - x - 1 = 0$
are also <u>$x = -0.6$ or $x = 1.6$</u>.

➤ Q & A

Use the graph of $y = x^2 + x - 3$
to solve $x^2 + x - 3 < 0$.

Answer

You have to find the values of x that
make $y < 0$. These are given by the
coloured part of the graph, i.e. the bit
below the x-axis.

The solution is <u>$-2.3 < x < 1.3$</u>.

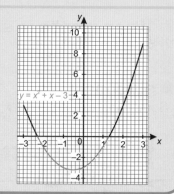

---

1 Use the graph of $y = x^2 - x - 4$ to solve $x^2 - 3x + 1 = 0$.
2 Use the graph of $y = x^2 - x - 4$ to solve $x^2 - x - 4 > 0$.

TEST

Graphs you should know (1)

You need to be able to <u>recognise</u> all the graphs on these two pages.
You also need to be able to <u>sketch</u> them from their equations.

● Straight lines

Any graph with equation
$y = mx + c$ is a <u>straight line</u>.

Make sure you can recognise
these special cases:

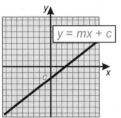

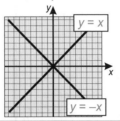

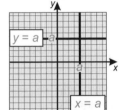

● Quadratics

Any graph with equation
$y = ax^2 + bx + c$ is a
<u>quadratic</u>.

You need to know what
$y = x^2$ and $y = -x^2$ look like.

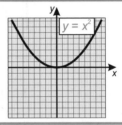

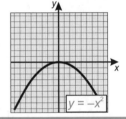

● Cubics

Any graph with equation
$y = ax^3 + bx^2 + cx + d$ is a
<u>cubic</u>.

You need to know what
$y = x^3$ and $y = -x^3$ look like.

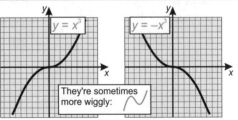

They're sometimes
more wiggly:

● Exponentials

'Something' to the power 'x'.

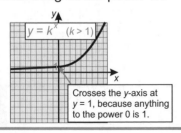

Crosses the y-axis at
$y = 1$, because anything
to the power 0 is 1.

● Reciprocals

'Something' over 'x'.

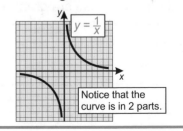

Notice that the
curve is in 2 parts.

54

Speedy Revision

Graphs you should know (2)

● $y = \sin x$

① It goes through the origin (0, 0).

② It has a maximum y-value of +1 and a minimum of −1.

③ It repeats every 360°.

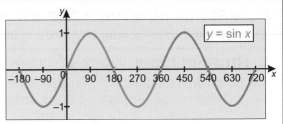

This is often called a 'sine wave'.

● $y = \cos x$

This is the same as the graph for sin, but it is shifted 90° to the left.

If nothing else, remember that it goes through (0, 1).

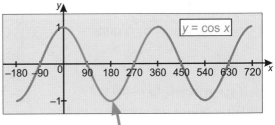

Notice that it starts with a 'valley' shape.

● $y = \tan x$

This one's a bit weird.

① It goes through (0, 0).

② It goes off to + and − infinity either side of 'asymptotes' (these are at 90°, 270°, etc).

③ It repeats every 180°.

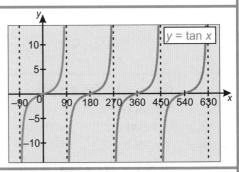

● It's so easy to make a mistake ...

... so always check your sketch by working out a few points.
For example, if you've been asked to sketch $y = \cos x$, quickly work out cos 0°, cos 90°, cos 180° and cos 360° on your calculator.

Cover all the graphs on these two pages. Now sketch these:

a $x = -3$ b $y = x$ c $y = -x$ d $y = x^2$

e $y = -x^2$ f $y = x^3$ g $y = -x^3$ h $y = \frac{1}{x}$

i $y = 2^x$ j $y = \sin x$ k $y = \cos x$ l $y = \tan x$

TEST

Graph transformations (1)

● Function notation – don't let it scare you

$y = f(x)$ looks scary, but it just means $y = $ 'an expression involving x'.

● There are four types of graph transformation

The y-shift and y-stretch are the easiest to remember.
The x-shift and x-stretch are a bit odd as they go the
opposite way to what you might expect.

❶ $y = f(x) \pm a$ (y-shift)

This is where the graph shifts up
or down the y-axis by a units.

$y = f(x) + a$ is $y = f(x)$ shifted
a units up.

$y = f(x) - a$ is $y = f(x)$ shifted
a units down.

The graph on the right shows
$y = f(x) + 2$, i.e. $y = x^2 + 2$ and
$y = f(x) - 4$, i.e. $y = x^2 - 4$.

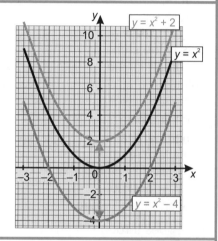

❷ $y = f(x \pm a)$ (x-shift)

This is where the graph shifts left or right along the x-axis by a units.
(Be careful because the graph moves in the opposite direction to
what you might think.)

$y = f(x + a)$ is $y = f(x)$ shifted a units to the left.
$y = f(x - a)$ is $y = f(x)$ shifted a units to the right.

The graph shows
$y = f(x + 2)$,
i.e. $y = (x + 2)^2$
and $y = f(x - 4)$,
i.e. $y = (x - 4)^2$.

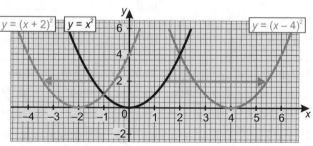

Speedy Revision

Graph transformations (2)

❸ $y = k \times f(x)$ (y-stretch)

This is where the graph <u>stretches parallel to the y-axis</u> by a factor of <u>k</u>. (When $k < 1$ the graph is squashed.)

The graph shows
$y = k \times f(x)$ <u>when $k > 1$</u>,
i.e. $y = 2 \times \sin x$
and also <u>when $k < 1$</u>,
i.e. $y = \frac{1}{2} \times \sin x$.

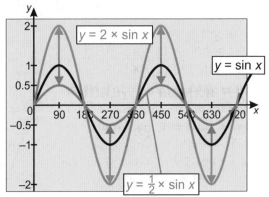

❹ $y = f(kx)$ (x-stretch)

This is where the graph <u>stretches parallel to the x-axis</u>.
But <u>be extremely careful</u> because the graph <u>squashes when $k > 1$</u>, and <u>stretches when $k < 1$</u>.

The graph shows
$y = f(kx)$ <u>when $k > 1$</u>,
i.e. $y = (2x)^2$
and also <u>when $k < 1$</u>,
i.e. $y = (\frac{1}{2}x)^2$.

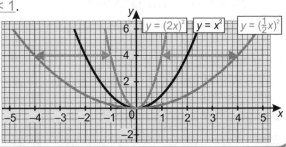

---

1 The graph shows $y = f(x)$.
Sketch the graphs of
 a $y = f(x) + 3$ **b** $y = f(x - 2)$
 c $y = f(2x)$ **d** $y = 2f(x)$.

2 Sketch the graphs of
 a $y = \cos(x - 180°)$ **b** $y = x^3 + 4$
 c $y = (x + 4)^3$ **d** $y = \cos 2x$
 e $y = \cos \frac{1}{3}x$ **f** $y = 3 \sin x$.

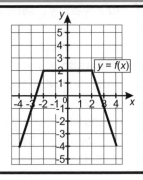

TEST

Real-life graphs (1)

● Distance–time graphs

In a distance–time graph the gradient gives the velocity (speed).

➤ Q & A

The graph shows Jo's car journey from her house to her sister's house, and then back home.

a How far away does Jo's sister live?

b What happened between 8.15am and 8.30am?

c When was Jo travelling fastest and what was her speed?

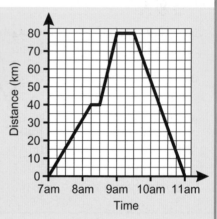

Answer

a 80 km   **b** She stopped (possibly to get petrol)

c Between 8.30am and 9am (steepest bit); 40 km ÷ 0.5 h = 80 km/h

● Velocity–time graphs

In a velocity–time graph the gradient gives the acceleration.

➤ Q & A

The graph shows Mrs Smith's speed as she runs for a bus.

Describe her journey in words.

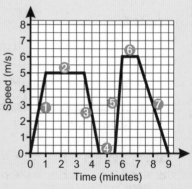

Answer

❶ From a standing start she picks up speed (accelerates).

❷ She then runs at a steady speed.

❸ She slows to a stop (❹), perhaps because she has to cross a road.

❺ She accelerates.

❻ She runs at a steady speed.

❼ She slows down as she approaches the bus stop.

58

Real-life graphs (2)

● Filling bottles with water

➤ Q & A

Sketch a graph to show the depth of water in this bottle as it is filled.

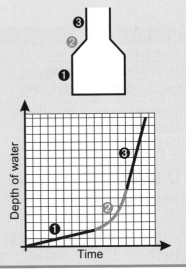

Answer

❶ The bottle is <u>wide</u> at the bottom, so it <u>fills slowly</u> at first.

❷ This part of the bottle <u>slopes</u>, so the graph will be <u>curved</u>.

❸ The bottle is <u>narrowest</u> here so the graph is <u>steepest</u>.

---

1 Look at the distance–time graph on page 58.

   a Work out the total distance that Jo travelled.

   b What was Jo's speed between 7am and 8.15am?

2 Look at the velocity–time graph on page 58.

   a When was Mrs Smith running the fastest? What was her speed?

   b Work out her acceleration in the first minute.

   c Work out her acceleration in the ninth minute.

3 Sketch graphs to show how the depth of water changes as these bottles are filled.

   a   **b**   **c**   **d**

TEST

Direct & inverse proportion

Questions on <u>direct or inverse proportion</u> are easy to spot. They all contain the phrase '<u>is proportional to</u>' or '<u>is inversely proportional to</u>'.

There are <u>4 basic cases</u> that you are likely to meet:

Phrase to look for	Rewrite using $\propto$	Replace $\propto$ with '= k'
❶ y is <u>proportional</u> to x	$y \propto x$	$y = kx$
❷ y is <u>proportional to the square</u> of x	$y \propto x^2$	$y = kx^2$
❸ y is <u>inversely proportional</u> to x	$y \propto \dfrac{1}{x}$	$y = \dfrac{k}{x}$
❹ y is <u>inversely proportional to the</u> <u>square</u> of x	$y \propto \dfrac{1}{x^2}$	$y = \dfrac{k}{x^2}$

$\boxed{\propto \text{ means 'is proportional to'.}}$

➤ Q & A

R is proportional to Q.
When R is 35, Q is 10.
What is R when Q is 70?

Answer

$R \propto Q$

This gives $R = kQ$

$35 = k \times 10$ [put $R = 35$ & $Q = 10$]
so $k = 35 \div 10 = 3.5$

Then $R = 3.5Q$

When $Q = 70$, $R = 3.5 \times 70 = \underline{245}$.

➤ Method

❶ Rewrite using $\propto$.
❷ Replace $\propto$ with '$\underline{= k}$'.
❸ Use information given in question to <u>find k</u>.
❹ Use the formula to answer the question.

If the 1st line of the **Q & A** had been 'R is inversely proportional to Q', then the equation would have been $R = \dfrac{k}{Q}$.

You would then complete the question in the same way as before. Go on, have a go!   (You should get $k = 350$, and a final answer of $R = 5$.)

1 s is directly proportional to the square of t.
   When s is 198, t is 6. What is s when $t = 2.8$?
2 The force of attraction between two magnets is inversely proportional to the square of the distance between them.
   When the magnets are 50 cm apart, the force is 16 N.
   How far apart are they when the force of attraction is 64 N?

TEST

60

Sequences

● Linear sequences

The <u>difference</u> between <u>consecutive terms</u> is the <u>same</u>.

➤ Q & A

a What are the next two terms of this sequence?
5, 7, 9, 11, ...

b What is the nth term?

c What is the 100th term?

Answer

a 5 7 9 11 13 15
+2 +2 +2 +2 +2

b nth term = $2n + 3$

Common difference is <u>2</u>.   First term is $2 + 3 = 5$

c Substituting $n = 100$ into nth term: $2 \times 100 + 3 = \underline{203}$

➤ Method for nth term

❶ Find the <u>common difference</u>, d.
Write 'nth term = dn'.

❷ What do you need to <u>add/subtract</u> to/from d to get the <u>first term</u>? Add/subtract this to dn to complete the <u>nth term</u>.

● Quadratic sequences

If the difference between terms isn't constant, the sequence may be quadratic. This just means it's <u>related to</u> the sequence of square numbers: <u>1, 4, 9, 16, ...</u>

➤ Q & A

Find the nth term of:
a 2, 5, 10, 17, ...
b 2, 8, 18, 32, ...

Answer

➤ Method

❶ See what you would have to do to <u>each square number</u> to get these terms.

❷ Do this to n^2. You have found the <u>nth term</u>.

a Square numbers $\underline{+\ 1}$, so nth term = $n^2 \underline{+\ 1}$

b <u>Double</u> square numbers, so nth term = $\underline{2n^2}$

Tip: The number in front of n^2 is always <u>half</u> the <u>second difference</u>.

Find the next term, the nth term and the 100th term:
a 2, 5, 8, 11, ...   **b** 10, 5, 0, –5, ...   **c** 0, 3, 8, 15, ...

TEST

Symmetry & properties of shapes (1)

● Reflection symmetry

If a shape can be folded so that one half fits exactly on the other, it is said to have <u>reflection symmetry</u> (also known as <u>line symmetry</u>).

Fold line (also called mirror line)

Some shapes have more than one line of symmetry; some don't have any:

Square
4 lines of symmetry

Equilateral triangle
3 lines of symmetry

No lines of symmetry

● Plane symmetry

This is basically <u>reflection</u> symmetry in <u>3-D shapes</u>.
A plane of symmetry cuts a solid shape in half so that one half is the mirror image of the other.

➤ **Q & A**   Draw a cube and an isosceles triangular prism.
Indicate one plane of symmetry in each.

Answer

Both of these shapes have more than one plane of symmetry. See TEST Q2 on page 63.

● Rotation symmetry

A shape has rotation symmetry if it looks exactly the same when turned. The <u>order of rotation symmetry</u> is the number of times a shape fits exactly over itself during a full-turn about its centre.

➤ **Q & A**

What is the order of rotation symmetry of these shapes?

<u>Order 4</u>   <u>Order 3</u>   <u>Order 1</u>

Note: Order of rotation symmetry 1 means <u>no rotation symmetry</u>.

Symmetry & properties of shapes (2)

● Four types of triangle

Right-angled
One 90° angle

Equilateral
3 equal sides
3 equal angles
3 lines of symmetry
Rotation symmetry of order 3

Isosceles
2 equal sides
2 equal angles
1 line of symmetry

Scalene
All sides and angles
are different

● Quadrilaterals (shapes with 4 sides)

Square
4 lines of symmetry
Rotation symmetry
of order 4
All angles are 90°
All sides equal
2 pairs of parallel sides

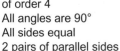

Rhombus
2 lines of symmetry
Rotation symmetry
of order 2
All sides equal
Opposite angles equal
2 pairs of parallel sides

Rectangle
2 lines of symmetry
Rotation symmetry
of order 2
All angles are 90°
Opposite sides equal
2 pairs of parallel sides

Kite
1 line of symmetry
No rotation symmetry
2 pairs of adjacent sides
equal
1 pair of opposite angles equal

Parallelogram
No lines of symmetry
Rotation symmetry
of order 2
Opposite sides
equal and parallel
Opposite angles equal

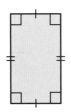

Trapezium
No lines of symmetry
(unless isosceles)
No rotation symmetry
One pair of parallel sides

Parallel lines never meet.
Perpendicular lines cross at right angles.

Angles & parallel lines

● Angles

Acute angles are between 0° and 90°.

Obtuse angles are between 90° and 180°.

Reflex angles are between 180° and 360°.

Angles on a straight line add up to 180°.

$a + b = 180°$

Angles at a point add up to 360°.

$c + d + e + f = 360°$

Vertically opposite angles are equal.

$p = r$ and $q = s$

● Parallel lines

Alternate angles are equal.

$u = v$

(The angles are in a Z-shape.)

Corresponding angles are equal.

$w = x$

(The angles are in an F-shape.)

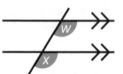

Supplementary angles add up to 180°.

$y + z = 180°$

(The angles are in a C-shape.)

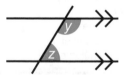

Work out the size of the lettered angles.

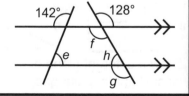

TEST

Polygons

● **The angles in a triangle add up to 180°**

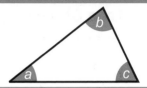

$$a + b + c = 180°$$

● **The angles in a quadrilateral add up to 360°**

$$w + x + y + z = 360°$$

● **Interior and exterior angles**

The angles <u>inside</u> a polygon are called <u>interior angles</u>.

<u>Exterior angles</u> are found on the <u>outside</u> when the <u>sides are extended</u>.

<u>Learn</u> these two formulae:

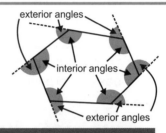

exterior angles

interior angles

exterior angles

❶ Sum of exterior angles = 360°

❷ Sum of interior angles = (number of sides − 2) × 180°

● **Regular polygons**

The <u>sides and angles</u> of a <u>regular polygon</u> are all the <u>same size</u>.

➤ **Q & A**

What is the size of an interior angle in a regular pentagon?

?

Answer

Using formula ❷ above we get:

Sum of interior angles of a regular pentagon = (5 − 2) × 180° = 540°

There are 5 equal interior angles, so size of one = 540° ÷ 5 = <u>108°</u>

---

1 What size are the interior and exterior angles of:
   a a square   **b** a regular hexagon   **c** a decagon?

2 The interior angle of a regular polygon is 175°.
   How many sides does the regular polygon have?

TEST

Areas of triangles & quadrilaterals

● Area of a triangle

Area = $\frac{1}{2}$ × base × height

$A = \frac{1}{2} \times b \times h$

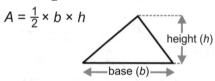

You may need to use this alternative formula:

Area = $\frac{1}{2} \times ab \sin C$

● Area of a rectangle

Area = length × width

$A = l \times w$

● Area of a parallelogram

Area = base × perpendicular height

$A = b \times h$

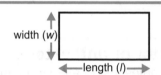

● Area of a trapezium

Area = $\frac{1}{2}$ × sum of parallel sides × height between them

$A = \frac{1}{2} \times (a + b) \times h$

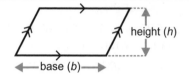

Essential: for triangles, parallelograms and trapeziums make sure that you use the height that's at right angles to the base.

Memorise the formulae above (get someone to test you), then work out the areas of these shapes (remember your units):

a
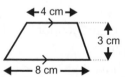

b

c
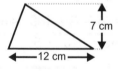

d
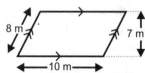

TEST

66

Circles

● Circumference

Circumference = 2 × π × radius

$$C = 2\pi r$$

radius

● Area

Area = π × radius squared

$$A = \pi r^2$$

π ≈ 3.14 (press **π** or, if asked to, leave your answer in terms of π)

➤ Example

Circumference = $2\pi r$ = 2 × **π** × 5 = <u>31.4 cm</u>

Area = πr^2 = **π** × 5^2 = <u>78.5 cm²</u>

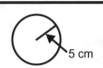
5 cm

● Parts of a circle

You need to learn all the names in these two diagrams.

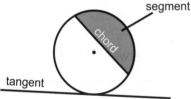
segment
chord
tangent

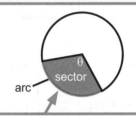
θ
sector
arc

Arc length = $\frac{\theta}{360°}$ × $2\pi r$

Sector area = $\frac{\theta}{360°}$ × πr^2

➤ Example

5 cm

Arc length = $\frac{90°}{360°}$ × $2\pi r$

= 0.25 × 2 × **π** × 5 = <u>7.85 cm</u>

Sector area = $\frac{90°}{360°}$ × πr^2

= 0.25 × **π** × 5^2 = <u>19.6 cm²</u>

Note: This is the <u>minor sector</u> (i.e. the small bit). The big bit is the <u>major sector</u>.

Use compasses to draw a circle of radius 3 cm.
1 What is the **a** circumference **b** area?
Use a protractor to mark a sector of angle 60°.
2 What is the **a** arc length **b** sector area?
3 Find the area of this segment.
   Leave your answer in terms of π.

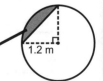
1.2 m

TEST

(Hint: Area of segment = area of sector − area of triangle.)

Composite shapes

● Perimeter

➤ Q & A
What is the perimeter of this shape?

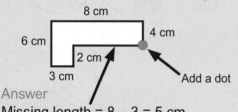

8 cm

6 cm

4 cm

2 cm

3 cm

Add a dot

> ### ➤ Method
> ❶ Work out any <u>missing lengths</u>.
> ❷ Mark a corner with a <u>dot</u>.
> ❸ <u>Add</u> the lengths in order, from dot to dot.

Answer

Missing length = 8 − 3 = 5 cm

Clockwise from the <u>dot</u>: 5 + 2 + 3 + 6 + 8 + 4 = <u>28 cm</u>

● Area

➤ Q & A
Work out the area of this shape:

Answer

The shape is a <u>semicircle</u> on top of a <u>triangle</u>.

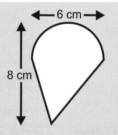

←6 cm→

8 cm

> ### ➤ Method
> ❶ Split into <u>simple shapes</u>.
> ❷ <u>Work out the area</u> of each shape.
> ❸ <u>Sum</u> to find the <u>total area</u>.

Area of semicircle = $\frac{1}{2} \times \pi \times 3^2$ = 14.14 cm²

Area of triangle = $\frac{1}{2} \times 5 \times 6$ = 15 cm²

Total area = 14.14 cm + 15 cm = <u>29.14 cm²</u>

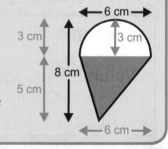

3 cm

8 cm

5 cm

←6 cm→

3 cm

←6 cm→

Work out the **i** perimeter **ii** area of each of these shapes:

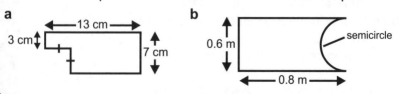

a

3 cm

←13 cm→

7 cm

b

0.6 m

semicircle

←0.8 m→

TEST

Volume & surface area (1)

● Volume of a cuboid

Volume = length × width × height

$V = l \times w \times h$

(This formula also works for a cube, i.e $V = l \times l \times l = l^3$)

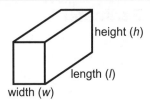

height (h)

length (l)

width (w)

● Volume of a prism

Volume = area of cross-section × length

$V = A \times l$

(A prism is a shape with the same cross-section all along its length.)

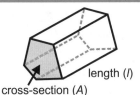

length (l)

cross-section (A)

● Volume & surface area of a cylinder

A cylinder is a prism with circular cross-section.

Volume = $\pi r^2 \times h$

Surface area = $2\pi r \times h + 2 \times \pi r^2$

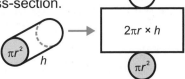

πr^2

$2\pi r \times h$

πr^2

πr^2

h

● Volume of a pyramid

Volume = $\frac{1}{3}$ × area of base × height

Tetrahedron

Square-based pyramid

● Volume & surface area of a cone

A cone is a pyramid with a circular base.

Volume = $\frac{1}{3} \times \pi r^2 \times h$

Curved surface area = $\pi r l$

Total surface area = $\pi r l + \pi r^2$

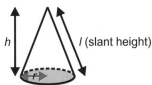

h

l (slant height)

r

● Volume & surface area of a sphere

Volume = $\frac{4}{3}\pi r^3$

Surface area = $4\pi r^2$

r

Volume & surface area (2)

➤ Q & A

Work out the volume of this triangular prism:

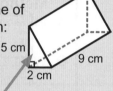

5 cm

9 cm

2 cm

Answer

The <u>area</u> of the <u>cross-section</u> (triangular end) is
$\frac{1}{2} \times 2 \times 5 = 5$ cm^2.

The <u>length</u> is 9 cm.

So <u>volume</u> = $A \times l$ = 5 × 9 = <u>45 cm^3</u>.

➤ **Method**

❶ Work out the <u>area</u> of the <u>cross-section</u>.

❷ Write down the <u>length</u> of the prism.

❸ Use the formula
$V = A \times l$
to work out the volume.

❹ Remember your <u>units</u> (usually cm^3 or m^3).

➤ Q & A

Work out the surface area of this cuboid.

Answer

First sketch the net of the cuboid.

The task now is to work out the area of each of the six rectangles (faces).

Two have an area of 2 cm × 3 cm = 6 cm^2
Two have an area of 2 cm × 4 cm = 8 cm^2
Two have an area of 3 cm × 4 cm = 12 cm^2

So the total surface area is
6 + 6 + 8 + 8 + 12 + 12 = <u>52 cm^2</u>.

3 cm   4 cm

2 cm

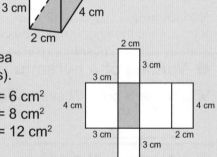

➤ Q & A

Work out the volume of this cylinder correct to 1 dp.

3 cm

10 cm

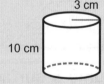

Answer

The radius is 3 cm and the height is 10 cm.
You simply put these numbers into the formula $V = \pi r^2 \times h$.

So the volume is $\pi \times 3^2 \times 10 = $ <u>282.7 cm^3</u>.

Remember your units.

Volume & surface area (3)

➤ Q & A

6 cm

Work out the
surface area
of this sphere:
Leave your answer in terms of π.

Answer

Surface area $= 4 \times \pi \times r^2$

$\qquad = 4 \times \pi \times 3^2$

$\qquad = \underline{36\pi \text{ cm}^2}$

➤ Method

❶ Write down the
   general formula.
❷ Write it again with the
   appropriate lengths in
   place of letters.
❸ Calculate the answer.
   (Leave it in terms of π if
   told to do so.)
❹ Remember your units.

➤ Q & A (A tricky one!)

Work out the volume of this frustum:
Leave your answer in terms of π.

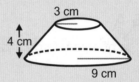

3 cm

4 cm

9 cm

Answer

A frustum is the shape made by cutting the top off a cone.
Start by using similar triangles to find the height of the whole cone.

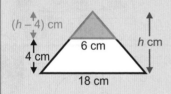

$(h - 4)$ cm

4 cm

6 cm

h cm

18 cm

$$\frac{h-4}{6} = \frac{h}{18} \quad \text{[similar triangles]}$$

$$18(h-4) = 6h$$

$$12h = 72$$

$$h = 6 \quad \text{[height of whole cone]}$$

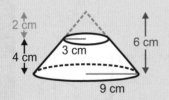

2 cm

4 cm

3 cm

6 cm

9 cm

Volume of whole cone $= \frac{1}{3} \times \pi \times 9^2 \times 6$

$\qquad = 162\pi \text{ cm}^3$

Volume of top cone $= \frac{1}{3} \times \pi \times 3^2 \times 2$

$\qquad = 6\pi \text{ cm}^3$

Volume of frustum = Volume of whole cone − Volume of top cone

$\qquad = 162\pi \text{ cm}^3 - 6\pi \text{ cm}^3$

$\qquad = \underline{156\pi \text{ cm}^3}$

Volume & surface area (4)

● Changing units

➤ Q & A

The volume of a cupboard is 4.5 m³.
What is the volume in cm³?

Answer

4.5 m³

= 4.5 (100 cm)³   [1 m = 100 cm]

= 4.5 × 100³ cm³

= 4.5 × 1 000 000 cm³

= <u>4 500 000 cm³</u>

➤ Method

❶ Write the area/volume down.

❷ Write it again with the <u>new length unit</u> in place of the <u>old length unit</u>.

❸ <u>Square</u> (for area) or <u>cube</u> (for volume) the new length unit.

❹ Multiply the numbers.

➤ Q & A

The area of a very large pizza is 8200 cm². What is the area in m²?

Answer

8200 cm²

= 8200 (0.01 m)²   [1 cm = 0.01 m]

= 8200 × 0.01² m²

= 8200 × 0.0001 m² = <u>0.82 m²</u>

---

1 Work out the volume of each of these shapes:

a 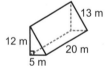 13 m, 12 m, 20 m, 5 m

b 8 cm, 9 cm, 9 cm

c 2 m, 4 m, 2 m

2 Work out the surface area of each of these shapes:

a 5 m, 6 m, 4.2 m

b 8.4 cm, 7 cm

c 20 cm, 6 cm

TEST

3 Change the units in your answer in **1a** to cm³ & **2b** to m².

Dimensions

● Length, area or volume?

The <u>dimensions</u> of a formula are the <u>number of lengths multiplied together</u> in each term.

❶ <u>Length</u> has <u>1 dimension</u>.

❷ <u>Area</u> terms are always <u>length × length</u>, so area has <u>2 dimensions</u>.

❸ <u>Volume</u> terms are always <u>length × length × length</u>, so volume has <u>3 dimensions</u>.

> **Example**

❶ l, w and h are lengths.

❷ hw, lw and hl are all areas (of faces).

❸ lwh is the volume.

> **Q & A**

p, q and r are all lengths.

Decide whether each expression is a length, area, volume or none of these.

> **Method**

❶ <u>Look at the first term</u>. Is it length, length × length or length × length × length? (Remember: length² means length × length.)

❷ <u>Check the other terms</u> are the same. If an expression is, e.g. length + area, it isn't a length or an area.

Answer

Expression	Type
$p + q$	<u>Length (2 terms, both lengths)</u>
3	<u>None (numbers have no dimensions)</u>
$10pq$	<u>Area (ignore any numbers multiplying lengths)</u>
$p + 2r$	<u>Length</u>
$8pr^2$	<u>Volume</u>
$q^2 + r^2$	<u>Area</u>
$pq + 5r$	<u>None (area + length)</u>
$pqr + p^3$	<u>Volume</u>

I've just come from another dimension.

Are these lengths, areas or volumes? (All letters are lengths.)
a $10a^2$ **b** $xyz + 2$ **c** $pq + qr + rs$ **d** π **e** $3u + 5t$ **f** $c^2d + cd^2$

TEST

Pythagoras' theorem (1)

- **The square of the hypotenuse is equal to the sum of the squares of the other two sides**

Using letters this is written as:

$$h^2 = a^2 + b^2$$

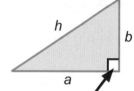

h is the hypotenuse, which is always the longest side (the side opposite the right angle).

Pythagoras' theorem only works in right-angled triangles.

- **Finding the hypotenuse (longest side)**

➤ **Q & A**

What is the length of the hypotenuse?

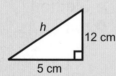

12 cm

5 cm

Answer

❶ $h^2 = 5^2 + 12^2$ [Pythagoras]

❷ $h^2 = 25 + 144 = 169$

❸ $h = \sqrt{169} = 13$

So the length of the hypotenuse is 13 cm.

➤ **Method**

❶ Write down Pythagoras' theorem for the given triangle.

❷ Add the squares of the shorter sides.

❸ Square root to find h.

- **Finding one of the shorter sides**

➤ **Q & A**

Find the missing length.

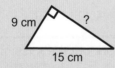

9 cm   ?

15 cm

Answer

❶ $15^2 = 9^2 + ?^2$ [Pythagoras]

i.e. $225 = 81 + ?^2$ [squaring]

❷ $?^2 = 225 - 81 = 144$

❸ $? = \sqrt{144} = 12$

So missing length is 12 cm.

➤ **Method**

❶ Write down Pythagoras' theorem for the given triangle.

❷ Rearrange to find the square of the missing side.

❸ Square root.

Pythagoras' theorem (2)

● Finding the distance between two points

➤ Q & A

Work out the distance between
the points P(2, 1) and Q(5, 3).

Answer

The line between the
points always makes the
hypotenuse of the triangle.

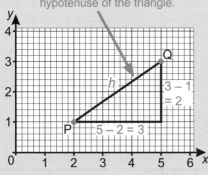

> ### ➤ Method
> ❶ <u>Sketch the two points</u>
>   with a <u>right-angled</u>
>   <u>triangle</u> drawn through
>   them.
> ❷ Work out the <u>lengths</u> of
>   the <u>shorter sides</u> of the
>   triangle (the horizontal
>   and vertical sides).
> ❸ Use Pythagoras'
>   theorem to work out the
>   <u>hypotenuse</u> (this is the
>   distance between the
>   two points).

From the diagram:

$h^2 = 3^2 + 2^2$ [Pythagoras]

$h^2 = 9 + 4$ [squaring]

$h^2 = 13$ [adding]

(You can use the √ button on your calculator to work out square roots.)

$h = \sqrt{13} = 3.6$ (to 1 dp)

So the distance between P and Q is <u>3.6 units</u>.

---

1 Use Pythagoras' theorem to work out the missing lengths.
Give your answers to 1 dp.

a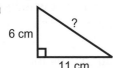
6 cm   ?   11 cm

b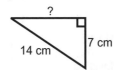
?   14 cm   7 cm

c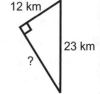
12 km   23 km   ?

2 Work out the distance between these points:
   a (4, 5) and (11, 13)   **b** (24, 11) and (12, −4)

Trigonometry (1)

Trigonometry and Pythagoras' theorem both involve right-angled triangles.
The difference is that trigonometry involves angles. Pythagoras only involves sides.

● Opposite & adjacent (& hypotenuse)

The first thing you should do when faced with a trig question is to label the sides of the triangle in relation to the angle you're interested in:

 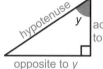

● Sine, cosine & tangent

$$\text{Sin } x = \frac{\text{Opposite}}{\text{Hypotenuse}} = \frac{O}{H}$$

$$\text{Cos } x = \frac{\text{Adjacent}}{\text{Hypotenuse}} = \frac{A}{H}$$

$$\text{Tan } x = \frac{\text{Opposite}}{\text{Adjacent}} = \frac{O}{A}$$

A good way to learn the trig ratios is to remember this 'word':

SOH-CAH-TOA

Or you could make up a phrase to remember like 'Silly Old Harry Caught A Herring Trawling Off America'...

● Finding an angle given two sides

➤ Q & A

Work out the size of angle w.

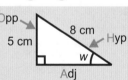

Answer

So Opp = 5 cm and Hyp = 8 cm.

SOH-CAH-TOA tells you that you need to use Sin, so:

$$\text{Sin } w = \frac{\text{Opp}}{\text{Hyp}} = \frac{5}{8} = 0.625$$

Now you have to find the inverse. You should have 0.625 on the screen (5 ÷ 8), so press [SHIFT] [sin] [=].

This gives $w = 38.7°$.

➤ Method

❶ Label sides Opp, Adj & Hyp in relation to the angle you want.

❷ Write down the two of Opp, Adj & Hyp you have been given.

❸ Use SOH-CAH-TOA to work out whether to use Sin, Cos or Tan.

❹ Find the inverse on your calculator.

Make sure you know how to find the inverse trig functions: $\sin^{-1}$, $\cos^{-1}$ and $\tan^{-1}$ on your calculator.

Trigonometry (2)

● Finding a side given an angle and another side

➤ Q & A

Work out the length of side AB.

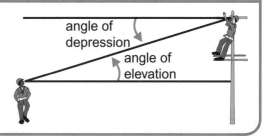

Hyp — 10 m   60°   Adj
C   Opp   B

Answer

So Hyp = 10 m, and we need to find AB which is Adj.

SOH-CAH-TOA tells you that you need to use Cos:

$$\text{Cos } 60° = \frac{\text{Adj}}{\text{Hyp}}$$

$$\therefore \text{Cos } 60° = \frac{AB}{10}$$

∴ 10 × Cos 60° = AB   [×10]

∴ AB = 10 × Cos 60°   [swap sides]

Work this out on your calculator by pressing [1] [0] [×] [cos] [6] [0] [=]. ◀── Check this works on your calculator. You may have to press: [1] [0] [×] [6] [0] [cos] [=].

This gives an answer of AB = 5 cm.

➤ Method

❶ Label sides Opp, Adj & Hyp in relation to the <u>angle you have been given</u>.

❷ Which of Opp, Adj & Hyp have you been given, and which do you have to find?

❸ Use SOH-CAH-TOA to work out whether to use Sin, Cos or Tan.

❹ Form an equation and solve it.

● Angle of elevation & depression

Angles of elevation or depression are measured from the horizontal up or down respectively.

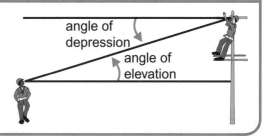

angle of depression

angle of elevation

---

1 Work out the sizes of the lettered angles and sides.

6 cm
10 cm   a

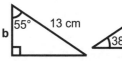
55°   13 cm
b

8 cm
38°
c

2 Lauren is 28 m from the base of a tree. The angle of elevation from ground level to the top of the tree is 35°. How tall is the tree? (Make a sketch then use trig.)

Trigonometry (3)

Before you attempt this page, sketch the graphs of $y = \sin x$, $y = \cos x$ and $y = \tan x$. (See page 55 if you've got no idea.)

● Angles of any size

➤ Q & A

Find the solutions to $\sin x = 0.5$, in the range $-360°$ to $360°$.

Answer

Using a calculator, the first solution is $x = 30°$. [$\sin^{-1} 0.5 = 30$]

Looking at the symmetry of the graph you should be able to see that the other solutions are 30° away from where the curve cuts the x-axis.

➤ Method

❶ Use your calculator to find the first solution.

❷ Sketch the graph of the trig function for the values required.

❸ Mark the first solution on the graph.

❹ Use symmetry to find the other solutions.

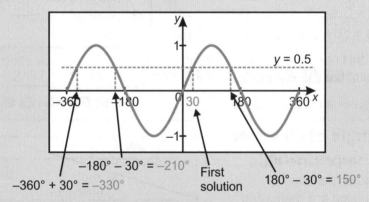

$-180° - 30° = -210°$

$-360° + 30° = -330°$

First solution

$180° - 30° = 150°$

So the full set of solutions is $x = 30°, 150°, -210°$ and $-330°$.

---

1 Find all the solutions to $\cos x = 0.342$ that are in the range $-360°$ to $360°$, giving your answers to the nearest degree.

2 Find all the solutions to

$$3 \sin x = 2$$

that are in the range 0° to 720°, giving your answers to 1 dp.

3 Find all the solutions to $\tan x = 1$ that are in the range $-360°$ to $360°$.

TEST

Sine & cosine rules (1)

The <u>sine and cosine rules</u> can be used on <u>any triangles</u> (they <u>don't</u> have to be right-angled). You may be given the formulae in the exam, but you should <u>learn them</u> – you'll find them much easier to use.

● Labelling triangles is as easy as ABC...

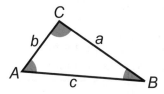

Label the <u>angles</u> with the CAPITAL letters <u>A, B and C</u>.

Label the <u>sides</u> with the lower-case letters <u>a, b and c</u>.

Make sure that <u>a is opposite A</u>, <u>b is opposite B</u>, and <u>c is opposite C</u>.

● The sine rule

There are <u>two forms</u> of the <u>sine rule</u>. Use the <u>first one</u> when you're looking for a <u>side</u>. The <u>second form</u> is the first turned upside-down; use it to find <u>angles</u>.

$$\frac{a}{\sin A} = \frac{b}{\sin B} = \frac{c}{\sin C}$$

$$\text{or} \quad \frac{\sin A}{a} = \frac{\sin B}{b} = \frac{\sin C}{c}$$

You don't need to use the whole of either formula, just pick out the two bits that you need, e.g. $\dfrac{b}{\sin B} = \dfrac{c}{\sin C}$ or $\dfrac{\sin A}{a} = \dfrac{\sin B}{b}$

The <u>sine rule is much easier to use than the cosine rule</u>, so use the sine rule as much as possible.

● The cosine rule

There are <u>two forms</u> of the <u>cosine rule</u>.

$$c^2 = a^2 + b^2 - 2ab \cos C$$

$$\text{or} \quad \cos C = \frac{a^2 + b^2 - c^2}{2ab}$$

Use the first form if you know <u>two sides and the enclosed angle</u> and need to <u>find the third side</u>.

Use the second form if you <u>know three sides</u> and need to <u>find an angle</u>.

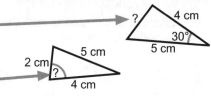

Use the <u>sine rule</u> for <u>all</u> other situations.

Sine & cosine rules (2)

> ### Method
> ❶ Label the sides _a, b_ and _c_, and the angles _A, B_ and _C_.
> ❷ Ask yourself 'Have I been given all 3 sides, or 2 sides and the enclosed angle?'.
>   If the answer is 'Yes', use the cosine rule.
>   If 'No', use the sine rule.
> ❸ Substitute the given numbers into the appropriate form of the rule. Rearrange to find the missing side or angle.

> ## Q & A (1)
Find the missing side.

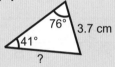

Answer

3.7 cm = _a_

The answer to ❷ is 'No', so use the sine rule.

Use the first form to find _b_.

$$\frac{a}{\sin A} = \frac{b}{\sin B}$$

$$\frac{3.7}{\sin 41°} = \frac{b}{\sin 76°}$$

so $b = \frac{3.7}{\sin 41°} \times \sin 76°$

$= \underline{5.5 \text{ cm}}$ to 1 dp

> ## Q & A (2)
Find the missing angle.

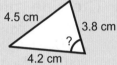

Answer

4.5 cm = _c_ , 3.8 cm = _a_ , 4.2 cm = _b_

3 sides given, so the answer to ❷ is 'Yes'. Use the cosine rule.

An angle is needed, so use the second form.

$$\cos C = \frac{a^2 + b^2 - c^2}{2ab}$$

$$\cos C = \frac{3.8^2 + 4.2^2 - 4.5^2}{2 \times 3.8 \times 4.2} = 0.37...$$

$C = \cos^{-1} 0.37... = \underline{68.2°}$ to 1 dp

Find the labelled sides and angles in these triangles.

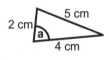

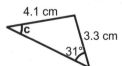

TEST

80

3-D Pythagoras & trigonometry

Examiners think flat stuff is pretty easy, so they're bound to throw a 3-D question at you. The trick is to <u>identify right-angled triangles</u>, then use <u>Pythagoras' theorem or normal trigonometry</u>. If you can't find any right-angled triangles, you'll have to use the <u>sine or cosine rule</u>.

➤ Q & A

ABCDEF is a right-angled triangular prism. Calculate:

a length ED **b** length DN
c angle EDN **d** length NC

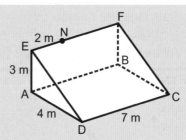

Answer

Start each part by sketching a suitable triangle:

a $ED^2 = 3^2 + 4^2 = 25$ [Pythagoras]
$ED = 5$ m [square root]

b $DN^2 = 2^2 + 5^2 = 29$ [Pythagoras]
$DN = 5.39$ m (2 dp) [square root]

c $\text{Tan } D = \dfrac{EN}{ED} = 0.4$
$D = \text{Tan}^{-1}\, 0.4 = 21.8°$

d $\angle NDC = 90° - 21.8° = 68.2°$

Triangle NDC is not right-angled, but we know two sides and the angle between so we can use the cosine rule.

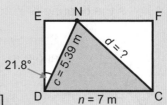

$d^2 = c^2 + n^2 - 2cn \cos D$ [cosine rule]
$= 5.39^2 + 7^2 - 2 \times 5.39 \times 7 \times \cos 68.2°$
$= 50.0$
$d = 7.07$ m (2 dp) [square root]

Note: You could have found d using Pythagoras' theorem on NF and FC.

Calculate

lengths **a** AH **b** BH

angles **c** EFH **d** BHF.

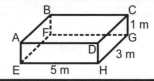

TEST

Bearings

● Three things you should know about bearings

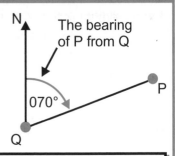

The bearing of P from Q

❶ A bearing is <u>an angle</u> that gives a <u>direction</u>.
❷ Bearings are measured <u>clockwise</u> from the <u>North line</u>.
❸ All bearings are given as 3 figures.

> ### Examples

Look for the word '<u>from</u>'. It tells you where to put the North line (i.e. where to measure <u>from</u>).

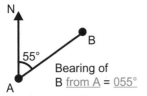

Bearing of B <u>from A</u> = <u>055°</u>

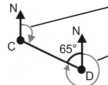

Bearing of D <u>from C</u>
= 180° − 65° = <u>115°</u>
(supplementary angles)

Bearing of C <u>from D</u>
= 360° − 65° = <u>295°</u>
(angles round a point)

● A typical bearings question (with trigonometry)

> ### Q & A

From airport X, a plane flies 130 km East, then 260 km South to airport Y.
What is the bearing of Y from X?

Answer

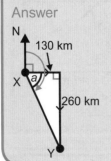

Start by working out angle a.

$$\text{Tan } a = \frac{\text{Opp}}{\text{Adj}} = \frac{260}{130} = 2$$

So $a = \text{Tan}^{-1}\, 2 = 63°$
(Work this out on your calculator.)

Bearing of Y from X
= 90° + 63° = <u>153°</u>

> ### Method

❶ Sketch a diagram (including a <u>right-angled triangle</u>).
❷ Use <u>trigonometry</u> to work out the angle or distance you need (see pages 76–77).
❸ Remember to give any bearings with 3 figures.

---

1 In the **Q & A** above, what is the bearing of X from Y?

2 A ship sails 58 km due North from point L. It then sails 43 km West to point M. What is the bearing of M from L?

TEST

Converting between measures

Learn all the conversions on this page then get someone to test you.

● Metric units

Length: 1 km = 1000 m, 1 m = 100 cm, 1 cm = 10 mm
Mass: 1 tonne = 1000 kg, 1 kg = 1000 g
Capacity: 1 litre = 1000 ml, 1 litre = 100 cl, 1 cl = 10 ml, 1 ml = 1 cm^3

● Imperial units

Length: 1 yard (yd) = 3 feet (ft), 1 foot (ft) = 12 inches (in)
Mass: 1 stone (st) = 14 pounds (lb), 1 pound (lb) = 16 ounces (oz)
Capacity: 1 gallon (gal) = 8 pints (pt)

● Metric to imperial

Length: 8 km ≈ 5 miles, 1 m ≈ 39 in, 30 cm ≈ 1 ft, 2.5 cm ≈ 1 in
Mass: 1 kg ≈ 2.2 pounds, 25 g ≈ 1 ounce
Capacity: 1 litre ≈ 1.75 pints, 4.5 litres ≈ 1 gallon

➤ Q & A

a What is 1200 m in km?
b What is 20 km in miles?

Answer

a 1000 m = 1 km   [fact]
       1 m = 0.001 km   [÷1000]
       1200 m = 1.2 km   [×1200]
b 8 km ≈ 5 miles   [fact]
       1 km = 0.625 miles [÷8]
       20 km = 12.5 miles [×20]

➤ Method

❶ Write down the most suitable conversion fact you know.
❷ Use it to find one unit.
❸ Multiply to find the number of units required.

---

1 Convert **a** 3 st to pounds (imperial) **b** 35 cl to litres (metric).
2 Convert between metric and imperial:
    a 45 cm to feet **b** 20 gallons to litres

TEST

Rounding measures

● Accuracy of measurement

Measurements are often given to the <u>nearest whole unit</u>.
The measurement could really be up to <u>half a unit more or less</u> than the given value.

> ### ➤ Example
>
> 17.5 cm, 17.9 cm, 18.2 cm and 18.4 cm all round to 18 cm to the nearest centimetre.
>
> The <u>smallest number</u> that rounds to 18 cm is 17.5 cm.
> The <u>largest number</u> that rounds to 18 cm is really 18.4999... cm, but this is a bit long-winded so we call the upper bound 18.5 cm.
>
> So <u>18 cm to the nearest cm</u> could be anything from <u>17.5 cm to 18.5 cm</u>.

➤ Q & A

The weight of a bag of seed is given as 2.7 kg to the nearest 100 g.

What are the lower and upper bounds for the weight of the bag?

Answer

➤ Method

❶ Decide what units to work in.
❷ <u>Check what accuracy</u> the measurement is given to.
❸ <u>Subtract half of this</u> from the measurement to find the <u>lower bound</u>.
❹ <u>Add half</u> to the measurement to find the <u>upper bound</u>.

In this case it's easiest to work in grams,
then convert back to kilograms at the end.

2.7 kg is 2700 g   100 g ÷ 2 = 50 g

Lower bound = 2700 g – 50 g = 2650 g = <u>2.65 kg</u>
Upper bound = 2700 g + 50 g = 2750 g = <u>2.75 kg</u>

Measurements are given to the accuracy shown in brackets.
Write down the lower and upper bounds.

a 43 hours (nearest hour)   **b** 27 pints (nearest pint)

c 2.8 cm (nearest mm)   **d** 9.2 litres (nearest 100 ml)

TEST

Calculating with rounded measures

● Addition & multiplication

Use the upper bounds of the values to get the upper bound of the calculation.
(Or the lower bounds for the lower bound of the calculation.)

> ### ➤ Example
> A rectangle is 3 m by 2 m.
> Max length   = 3.5 m
> Max width   = 2.5 m
> Max area   = 3.5 m × 2.5 m
>   = 8.75 m^2

● Subtraction & division

Be careful here! You will need to use an upper bound and a lower bound to find the upper bound of the calculation.
There are only four cases, so it's best to learn them:

Max (A − B) = Max A − Min B	Min (A − B) = Min A − Max B
Max (A ÷ B) = Max A ÷ Min B	Min (A ÷ B) = Min A ÷ Max B

But if in any doubt, try the Max and Min the other way round to see if the answer is bigger or smaller.

➤ Q & A

Alice is 162 cm tall. Tina is 158 cm tall. What is the minimum possible difference in their heights?

Answer

➤ Method

❶ Write down the upper and lower bounds for each measurement.
❷ Write down the required calculation.
❸ Pick out the values you will use.
❹ Do the calculation.

Alice is between 161.5 cm and 162.5 cm tall.
Tina is between 157.5 cm and 158.5 cm tall.

Min (Alice − Tina) = Min Alice − Max Tina
                    = 161.5 cm − 158.5 cm
                    = 3 cm

And just to check:
162.5 − 157.5 = 5 cm,
so the answer is right.

---

1 Find the minimum perimeter of a 14.2 mm (1 dp) square.

2 Suna runs 100 m in 15 s (both to nearest whole number). Find his maximum possible speed.

TEST

Compound measures

● **Speed = $\dfrac{\text{Distance}}{\text{Time}}$**

There are 3 ways of writing this formula:

$S = \dfrac{D}{T}$ $T = \dfrac{D}{S}$ $D = S \times T$

All 3 ways can be remembered using this 'formula triangle'.

➤ **Q & A**

A car travels at 70 mph for 2.5 hours. How far does it go?

Answer

Distance is needed so cover up D.

This gives D = S × T

D = 70 × 2.5 = 175

The car travels 175 miles.

➤ **Method**

❶ Cover up what you want on the formula triangle. Write down the formula this gives.

❷ Write the formula with the numbers you know. (Make sure the units match, e.g. if the speed has hours in it, the time must be in hours.)

❸ Calculate the unknown.

● **Density = $\dfrac{\text{Mass}}{\text{Volume}}$**

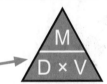

Like the one for speed, this formula can also be written in a 'formula triangle':

➤ **Q & A**

A block has a density of 22 kg/m³. The mass of the block is 88 kg. What is the volume of the block?

Answer

Volume is needed so cover up V.

This gives $V = \dfrac{M}{D}$

So $V = \dfrac{88}{22} = 4$

The block has a volume of 4 m³.

1 How long will a car travelling at 60 km/h take to travel 40 km?

2 Calculate the mass of 2 m³ of wood of density 500 kg/m³.

TEST

Circle theorems (1)

❶ Tangent and radius meet at right angles

The <u>tangent</u> at any point on a circle is <u>perpendicular</u> to the <u>radius</u> at that point.

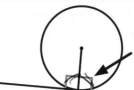

tangent and radius are at right angles (90°)

❷ Tangents from an external point are equal in length

PA = PB

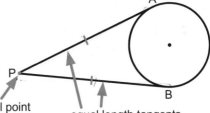

external point

equal length tangents

❸ A line drawn from the centre of a circle perpendicular to a chord bisects the chord

AB = BC

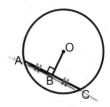

❹ Angle at centre is twice that at circumference

The <u>angle</u> subtended by an arc at the <u>centre</u> of a circle is <u>twice the angle</u> subtended at any point <u>on the remaining part of the circumference</u>.

❺ Angle at circumference of a semicircle is 90°

The angle subtended at the circumference by a semicircle is a right angle.

Basically, a <u>triangle</u> drawn from a <u>diameter</u> makes a <u>right angle at the edge</u> of the circle.

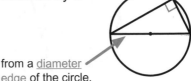

Circle theorems (2)

❻ Angles in the same segment are equal

Triangles drawn from a chord have the same angle where they meet the circumference.

The angles have to be on the <u>same side</u> of the chord.

❼ Opposite angles in a cyclic quadrilateral add up to 180°

$$a + c = 180°$$
$$b + d = 180°$$

A cyclic quadrilateral is a 4-sided shape whose corners are all on the circumference of a circle.

❽ Angle between tangent and chord equals angle in alternate segment

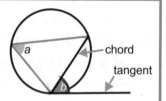

If a chord and tangent meet, then the angle between them equals the angle at the circumference on the other side of the chord.

$$a = b$$

<u>Memorise</u> everything on pages 87–88, then <u>write down</u> all you can remember.

Then work out the size of:

a ∠PRT
b ∠ORT

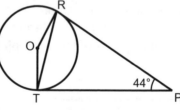

c ∠ACB
d ∠ADB
e ∠DAE

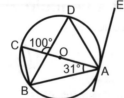

f ∠WXY
g ∠WZY

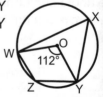

(Tip: if you get stuck just try applying each theorem one at a time.)

TEST

Speedy Revision

Circle theorems (3)

● Proving the circle theorems

You don't just have to know how to <u>use</u> the eight circle theorems, you also need to know how to <u>prove</u> the last five (❹❺❻❼❽). Honestly, this isn't as hard as it sounds. Just learn how to prove ❹ using triangles (see **Q & A**). The others then follow on from it.

➤ **Q & A**   Prove theorem ❹.

Answer

Join M to O and extend MO to N.

$\angle OMA = \angle OAM = x$
  (base angles of an isosceles triangle)

Then $\angle AON = x + x = 2x$
  (exterior angle of a triangle equals the
  sum of the two opposite interior angles)

Similarly, $\angle OMB = \angle OBM = y$ and $\angle BON = 2y$

$\angle AMB = x + y$

$\angle AOB = 2x + 2y = 2(x + y) = 2 \times \angle AMB$

So $\angle AOB = 2 \times \angle AMB$

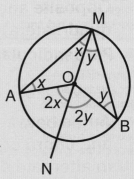

Always start by drawing and labelling a diagram.

---

1 Make sure you understand all the steps in the **Q & A** above, then close this page and write down the proof of ❹.

2 Prove theorem ❺ using ❹. (Hint: Use the fact that the angle at the centre of a diameter is 180°.)

3 Prove theorem ❻ using ❹.
(Hint: Draw the angle at the centre from the chord.)

4 Prove theorem ❼ using ❹.
(Hint: Start with this diagram and the fact that the angles at the centre add up to 360°.)

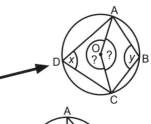

5 Prove theorem ❽ using ❺ & ❻.
(Hint: Start with this diagram and use ❺ on triangle ABC. Then use ❻ to prove that $\angle BCP = \angle BDC$.)

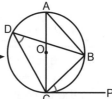

TEST

Constructions & loci (1)

● How to construct an equilateral triangle

1

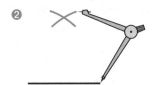

Draw a line of the length you want the sides to be, e.g. 5 cm.

2

Set your compasses to 5 cm. Draw two crossing arcs from the ends of the line.

3

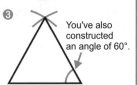

You've also constructed an angle of 60°.

Join the point where the arcs cross to the ends of the line.

● Perpendicular bisector of a line

Perpendicular means 'at right angles'. Bisect means 'cut in half'.

This is similar to constructing an equilateral triangle.

You just have to draw two more crossing arcs on the other side of the line.

Set your compasses to more than half the length of the line.

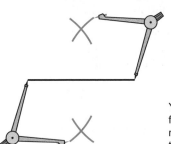

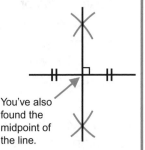

You've also found the midpoint of the line.

● Perpendicular from a point to a line

1 Draw two arcs on the line, centred on the point. Keep your compasses set at the same distance.

2 Draw two crossing arcs on the other side of the line, with the compasses centred on the arcs on the line.

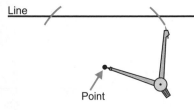

Line

Point

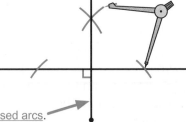

3 Draw a line from the point to the crossed arcs. This is the perpendicular from the point to the line.

---

1 Construct an equilateral triangle of side 6 cm.
2 Draw a line 8 cm long. Construct its perpendicular bisector.
3 Construct the perpendicular from a point to a line.

TEST

Speedy Revision

Constructions & loci (2)

● Perpendicular from a point **on a line**

❶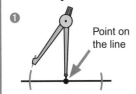
Point on the line

❷

❸

Draw arcs on the line <u>either side</u> of the point. Use the <u>same radius</u>.

<u>Increase</u> the radius. Draw <u>two crossing arcs</u> centred on the arcs on the line.

Join the <u>original point</u> to where the <u>arcs cross</u>. This is the perpendicular.

● Bisector of an angle

❶

❷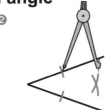

❸
The line cuts the angle in half.

Draw <u>two arcs</u> on the arms of the angle, <u>centred on the vertex</u>.

Draw <u>two crossing arcs</u> inside the angle, <u>centred on the arcs</u> on the arms.

Join the <u>vertex</u> to the point where the <u>arcs crossed</u>.

● Loci

A <u>locus</u> is a <u>set of points</u> (often lines) that <u>satisfy a given rule</u>. Here are <u>four loci</u> that you should <u>know</u> (loci are in colour):

❶

❷

❸

❹

A fixed distance from a point is a circle.

A fixed distance from a straight line is two parallel straight lines.

Equidistant from two points is the perpendular bisector of the line joining the two points.

Equidistant from two straight lines is the bisectors of the angles between the lines.

Types ❶ & ❷ are often combined:
Fixed distance from a line segment

1 Construct a perpendicular 5 cm from the end of a 14 cm line.
2 Draw a 68° angle with a protractor. Bisect it with compasses.
3 Construct the locus of points 4 cm from a line 6 cm long.

TEST

Congruent & similar shapes (1)

● Similar shapes

Similar shapes are exactly the same shape.

Congruent shapes are exactly the same shape *and* size.

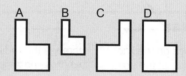

➤ Q & A

Which of these are similar, congruent or neither?

Answer

A and C are similar to B. A is congruent to C. D is neither.

● Similar shapes are enlargements of each other

➤ Q & A

These two triangles are similar. Calculate the missing lengths.

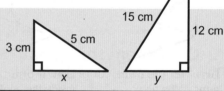

Answer

Use the hypotenuses to find the scale factor.

$$5 \text{ cm} \xrightarrow{\times 3} 15 \text{ cm}$$

So the s.f. is 3.

y is the shortest side so it corresponds to 3 cm:

$\underline{y} = 3 \text{ cm} \times 3 = \underline{9 \text{ cm}}$ ◀

That leaves x and 12 cm:

$\underline{x} = 12 \text{ cm} \div 3 = \underline{4 \text{ cm}}$ ◀

➤ Method

❶ Use the common length to find the scale factor (s.f.) that takes you from the small triangle to the large one.

❷ Multiply/divide by the s.f. to find the missing lengths.

Multiply when you are going from the small triangle to the large one.

Divide when going from large to small.

---

1 Are these similar, congruent or neither?

   a A and B   **b** A and C

2 D is similar to B. Find x.

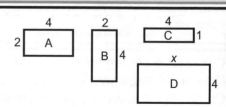

TEST

Speedy Revision

Congruent & similar shapes (2)

● Areas and volumes of similar shapes

When the <u>lengths</u> in a shape are enlarged by a <u>scale factor k</u>:

◆ the <u>area</u> is enlarged by <u>scale factor k^2</u>

◆ the <u>volume</u> is enlarged by <u>scale factor k^3</u>.

➤ Examples

A square that is enlarged by <u>scale factor 4</u>, will have sides 4 times longer, but an area $4^2 = 16$ times larger.

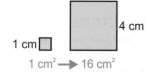

1 cm² ➜ 16 cm²

A cube that is enlarged by <u>scale factor 3</u>, will have sides 3 times longer, but a volume $3^3 = 27$ times larger.

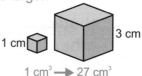

1 cm³ ➜ 27 cm³

● Congruent triangles

Two triangles are congruent if one of these conditions is true:

SSS Three pairs of sides are equal. 	SAS Two pairs of sides are equal and the angle between them is equal. 
AAS Two pairs of angles are equal and one pair of corresponding sides are equal. 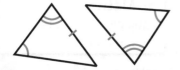	RHS Both triangles have a right angle, the hypotenuses are equal and one pair of corresponding sides is equal. 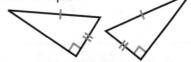

---

1 The ratio of the radii of two spheres is 1 : 4. Calculate the ratio of **a** the surface areas **b** the volumes of the spheres.

2 Write down the four conditions for congruent triangles. (Close this page first, obviously...)

TEST

Vectors (1)

● Vector notation

A vector can be written in different ways:

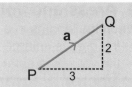

◆ with an <u>arrow</u> showing where the vector goes <u>from</u> (P) and <u>to</u> (Q)

◆ using a <u>bold or underlined letter</u>

◆ in a <u>column</u> showing <u>distance right</u> (3) and <u>distance up</u> (2).

$$\overrightarrow{PQ} = \mathbf{a} = \underline{a} = \begin{bmatrix} 3 \\ 2 \end{bmatrix}$$

Note: –**a** is the same length as **a** but it goes in the opposite direction, i.e. from Q to P.

● Adding & subtracting column vectors

➤ Q & A

$\mathbf{u} = \begin{bmatrix} -6 \\ 3 \end{bmatrix}$, $\mathbf{v} = \begin{bmatrix} 5 \\ 8 \end{bmatrix}$

Find **u** + **v** and **u** – **v**.

Answer

➤ Method

❶ Add/subtract the <u>top numbers</u>.

❷ Add/subtract the <u>bottom numbers</u>.

$$\mathbf{u} + \mathbf{v} = \begin{bmatrix} -6 \\ 3 \end{bmatrix} + \begin{bmatrix} 5 \\ 8 \end{bmatrix} = \begin{bmatrix} -6 + 5 \\ 3 + 8 \end{bmatrix} = \begin{bmatrix} -1 \\ 11 \end{bmatrix}$$

The <u>sum of two vectors</u> is sometimes called the '<u>resultant vector</u>'.

$$\mathbf{u} - \mathbf{v} = \begin{bmatrix} -6 \\ 3 \end{bmatrix} - \begin{bmatrix} 5 \\ 8 \end{bmatrix} = \begin{bmatrix} -6 - 5 \\ 3 - 8 \end{bmatrix} = \begin{bmatrix} -11 \\ -5 \end{bmatrix}$$

● Multiplying column vectors by a 'scalar'

You can't multiply vectors together, but you can multiply a vector by a 'scalar' (i.e. any number).

➤ Q & A

Find 3**p**, where $\mathbf{p} = \begin{bmatrix} 4 \\ 5 \end{bmatrix}$.

Answer

➤ Method

Multiply top and bottom by the number.

$$3\mathbf{p} = 3 \times \begin{bmatrix} 4 \\ 5 \end{bmatrix} = \begin{bmatrix} 3 \times 4 \\ 3 \times 5 \end{bmatrix} = \begin{bmatrix} 12 \\ 15 \end{bmatrix}$$

3**p** is <u>parallel</u> to **p** and <u>3 times as long</u>.

TEST

1 Using **u**, **v** and **p** above, find as column vectors –**u**, 3**p** – 2**v**.

2 What do you notice about your answer to **1**?

94

Vectors (2)

● Position vectors

The position vector of a point A is the
vector $\overrightarrow{OA}$, where O is the origin.

● Vector diagrams

You'll almost certainly get a question like this one in your exams!

➤ Q & A

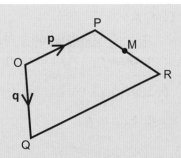

$\overrightarrow{OP}$ = **p**, $\overrightarrow{OQ}$ = **q**.

OP is parallel to QR.
QR is twice the length of OP.
M is the midpoint of PR

Find, in terms of **p** and **q**:

a $\overrightarrow{QR}$ **b** $\overrightarrow{PM}$

Answer

a QR is twice as long as OP and parallel to it, therefore:

$\overrightarrow{QR} = 2\overrightarrow{OP} = 2\mathbf{p}$

b M is the midpoint of PR, therefore $\overrightarrow{PM} = \frac{1}{2}\overrightarrow{PR}$.

Now $\overrightarrow{PR} = \overrightarrow{PO} + \overrightarrow{OQ} + \overrightarrow{QR}$ ◀—— Go from P to R the long way
round (via O then Q)

$= -\mathbf{p} + \mathbf{q} + 2\mathbf{p} = \mathbf{p} + \mathbf{q}$

So $\overrightarrow{PM} = \frac{1}{2}(\mathbf{p} + \mathbf{q})$

● The magnitude of a vector

Pythagoras' theorem!

The magnitude (length) of the vector $\begin{bmatrix} x \\ y \end{bmatrix}$ is $\sqrt{x^2 + y^2}$.

> ➤ The magnitude of **a** on page 94 is $\sqrt{3^2 + 2^2} = \sqrt{13}$.

---

1 ABCDEF is a regular hexagon.
Work out these vectors in terms of **x** and **y**:

a $\overrightarrow{AC}$ **b** $\overrightarrow{DA}$ **c** $\overrightarrow{AF}$

2 Work out the magnitude of **w** = $\begin{bmatrix} -5 \\ 12 \end{bmatrix}$.

TEST

Transformations (1)

A <u>transformation</u> maps the <u>object</u> (original shape) to an <u>image</u> (a new shape in a different position).

● Translation

A <u>translation</u> is defined by a <u>distance</u> and a <u>direction</u>.

A <u>vector</u> can be used to show the distance and direction.

➤ Q & A

a Describe the translation that takes A to B.

b Translate A by $\begin{bmatrix} -2 \\ -4 \end{bmatrix}$. Label the new shape A_1.

Answer

a A needs to move 6 left, 1 up to get to B. As a vector that's: $\begin{bmatrix} -6 \\ 1 \end{bmatrix}$ ⟵ Use a <u>minus</u> to show moves <u>left</u> or <u>down</u>.

b $\begin{bmatrix} -2 \\ -4 \end{bmatrix}$ ⟵ <u>Minus</u> 2 means <u>left</u> 2.

<u>Minus</u> 4 means <u>down</u> 4.

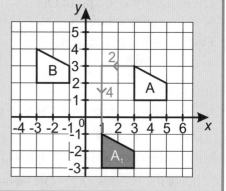

● Reflection   A <u>reflection</u> is defined by a <u>mirror line</u>.

➤ Q & A

Reflect A in the line $x = 1$.
Label the new shape A_2.

> ### ➤ Method
> ❶ Draw the <u>mirror line</u>.
> ❷ Draw lines from the corners of A to the mirror line <u>at right angles</u>.
> ❸ Draw the corners of A_2 the <u>same distance</u> from the mirror line.

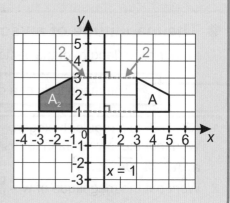

Transformations (2)

● Rotation

A rotation is defined by its centre and an anticlockwise angle.

These can be quite hard, so always use tracing paper to help you.

➤ **Q & A**

a Rotate A through 90°
about (3, 3).
Label the new shape A_3.

b Describe the rotation
that takes A to C.

Answer

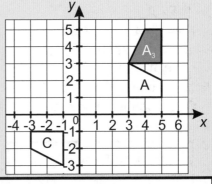

a

> ### ➤ Method for a
> ❶ Trace shape A.
> ❷ Put the point of your
>   pencil on the centre of
>   rotation and rotate A
>   anticlockwise through
>   the given angle.
> ❸ Draw and label A_3.

> ### ➤ Method for b
> ❶ Guess the centre of rotation.
> ❷ Use tracing paper and the
>   method for **a** to see if you
>   are right.
> ❸ If not, keep guessing.
>   (Your guesses will improve
>   with practice.)

b Rotation through 180°
about (1, 0)

---

1 Describe the transformation from P to
   a Q **b** R **c** S.

2 Copy the axes and shape Q.
   a Translate Q by $\begin{bmatrix} 5 \\ -2 \end{bmatrix}$.
   b Reflect Q in $y = x + 1$.
   c Rotate Q through 90°
        about (−1, 0).

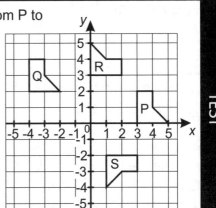

TEST

Transformations (3)

● Enlargement

An <u>enlargement</u> changes the <u>size</u> of an object, but not its shape.
To describe an enlargement you give its <u>centre</u> and <u>scale factor</u>.

➤ Q & A

a Enlarge A by a scale factor of 2 about (−1, 1). Label the image B.

b D is an enlargement of C. Describe the enlargement.

Answer

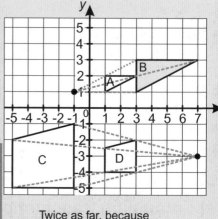

Twice as far, because the scale factor is 2.

a

> ### ➤ Method for a
> ❶ <u>Draw 'rays'</u> from the centre of enlargement through the vertices of A.
> ❷ Draw the vertices of B on these rays, <u>twice as far</u> from the centre.

b Enlargement with scale factor $\frac{1}{2}$, centre (7, −3)

D is half the size of C.

> ### ➤ Method for b
> ❶ <u>Draw 'rays'</u> through corresponding vertices. The point where these cross is the <u>centre</u>.
> ❷ Measure <u>corresponding lengths</u> to find the scale factor.

---

1 Draw axes with both x and y from −10 to 10.

   a Plot these points. Join them in order. Label the shape A.
   (−5, −1), (−7, −5), (−5, −3), (−1, −5), (−5, −1)

   b Enlarge A using
   i centre (−7, −9), s.f. 2   **ii** centre (−7, −9), s.f. $\frac{1}{2}$.

2 Look again at the **Q & A**.
   Describe the transformation from **a** B to A   **b** D to C.

TEST

Transformations (4)

● Enlargement with a negative scale factor

If the <u>scale factor is negative</u>, the image will be on the <u>opposite side</u> of the centre of enlargement to the object.

> **Example**   F is an enlargement of E by a <u>scale factor of –2</u> with centre (3, 4).

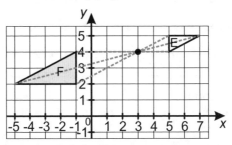

● Combining transformations

In the exam you might be asked to spot a combination of transformations. If the image is <u>not congruent</u> (same size and shape) to the object then you know that an <u>enlargement</u> is involved. Often there is more than one combination of transformations that work.

> **Example**

You can get from G to H by <u>reflecting G in the y-axis</u> and then <u>translating by</u> $\begin{bmatrix} 0 \\ -6 \end{bmatrix}$.

Or you could <u>reflect G in the x-axis</u> and then <u>rotate by 180° about (0, –3)</u>.

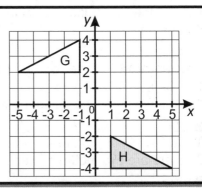

Draw axes with both x and y from –10 to 10.

a Plot these points. Join them in order. Label the shape A.
(–4, 1), (–7, –5), (–4, –2), (–1, –5), (–4, 1)

b Enlarge A using centre (–4, 1), s.f. –1.

TEST

Mean, median, mode, range

Mean = $\dfrac{\text{total of the values}}{\text{number of values}}$

You need to learn these.

Median = **the middle value when the numbers are put in order of size**

Mode = **the most common value**

Range = **highest value – lowest value**

When people talk about 'the average' they're usually referring to 'the mean'. But be careful, because the median and mode are also 'averages'.

➤ Q & A

Find the mean, median, mode and range of this set of data:

5, 1, 3, 1, 5, 5, 10, 3, 3

Answer

Mean
The total of the values = 5 + 1 + 3 + 1 + 5 + 5 + 10 + 3 + 3 = 36
The number of values = 9 (count the numbers in the list)
So the mean = 36 ÷ 9 = 4.

Median
Rearrange the numbers in order of size.
1, 1, 3, 3, 3, 5, 5, 5, 10
The middle number is 3, so the median = 3.

> If there are an even number of values, the median is halfway between the middle two.
> e.g. the median of 2, 3, 4, 5 is (3 + 4) ÷ 2 = 3.5.

Mode
3 and 5 are most common.
So there are two modes = 3 and 5.

Range
The highest value = 10 and the lowest value = 1.
So the range = 10 – 1 = 9.

Find the mode, median, mean and range of this set of data:
0.7, 1.2, 1.5, 1.2, 1.2, 1.6, 1.0, 0.8, 0.7

TEST

Two-way tables; stem & leaf diagrams

● Two-way tables

Two-way tables show two sets of information in one table.

> **Example** This two-way table shows the number of DVDs and CDs owned by a group of friends.

	DVDs	CDs	Total
Boys own	2	9	11
Girls own	18	31	49
Total	20	40	60

Boys own 9 CDs

Girls own 18 DVDs

There is a total of 60 DVDs and CDs

● Stem & leaf diagrams

These are like <u>bar charts</u>, but each bar displays the <u>actual data</u>.

> **Example**

This data is shown on the stem and leaf diagram below:
4, 5, 8, 12, 18, 19, 20, 22, 24, 25, 25, 26, 31, 32, 34, 36, 40, 43, 44

The 'stem' is the first part of the number, in this case Tens.

The 'leaf' is the rest of the number, in this case Units.

0	4	5	8			
1	2	8	9			
2	0	2	4	5	5	6
3	1	2	4	6		
4	0	3	4			

The <u>leaves</u> should be given in <u>order of size</u>. If the original list of data had been jumbled you would have had to re-order the leaves.

Always include a key. → Key: 1 | 8 means 18

Mode = most common value = 25 (because 2 | 5 appears twice)
Median = 10th value = 25 (count along the rows, starting at the top)

---

1 Complete this two-way table that shows the colours of pens owned by a group of friends.

	Black	Red	Blue	Total
Boys own	14		11	26
Girls own	7	7		34
Total	21	8	31	60

2 Show these test marks on a stem and leaf diagram:
50, 75, 51, 68, 72, 48, 62, 58, 65, 62, 42, 70, 54, 67, 60, 73, 74, 69, 62, 59, 63, 72, 62, 63, 57, 69, 49, 56, 58, 70

TEST

Speedy Revision

Pie charts

● Drawing pie charts

➤ Q & A (1)

Draw a pie chart for this shopping budget.

Food	£31
Drinks	£12
Personal hygiene	£8
Cleaning products	£6
Other	£3

➤ Method

❶ <u>Add</u> up the amounts.
❷ Calculate 360° ÷ ❶.
❸ <u>Multiply</u> each amount by ❷.
❹ <u>Check</u> the angles add to 360°.
❺ <u>Draw and label</u> the sectors.

Answer

❶ The total amount is £60.

❷ 360 ÷ 60 = 6

Item	Amount	Angle ❸
Food	£31	31 × 6 = 186°
Drinks	£12	12 × 6 = 72°
Personal hygiene	£8	8 × 6 = 48°
Cleaning products	£6	6 × 6 = 36°
Other	£3	3 × 6 = 18°
Total	£60	360° ❹

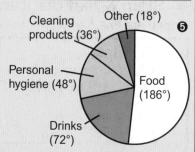

Tip: when using a 180° protractor, it is often easier to draw the small angles first.

● Reading pie charts

➤ Q & A (2)

Out of 30 students, how many watched a film?

Answer

The Film sector is 120°.

It is $\frac{120°}{360°} = \frac{1}{3}$ of the chart.

$\frac{1}{3}$ of 30 = 30 ÷ 3 = 10 students watched a film.

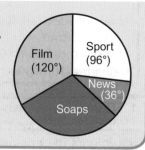

---

1 Show these colours on a pie chart:

Red 40, Blue 25, Green 15, Other 10

2 Look at **Q & A (2)**. How many watched the other programmes?

TEST

Speedy Revision

Time series & moving averages

● Time series graphs

➤ **Q & A**   This table shows a household's quarterly gas bills.

Year	1999				2000				2001			
Quarter	Q1	Q2	Q3	Q4	Q1	Q2	Q3	Q4	Q1	Q2	Q3	Q4
Charge (£)	85	45	55	79	96	47	58	83	94	52	59	89

a Plot the data as a time series.
b Comment on the graph.
c Plot the 4-point moving average.
d Comment on the trend.

Answer

— Time series
— Moving average

a

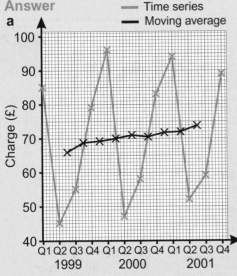

➤ **Method for 4-point moving average (M.A.)**

❶ Find the <u>mean of the 1st to 4th</u> values.

❷ Find the <u>mean of the 2nd to 5th</u> values.

❸ Continue finding the means, <u>moving on one quarter at a time</u>.

❹ Plot each mean in the <u>middle of the 4 points</u> used.

b High charges in Q1 and Q4 reflect colder months.

c 1st M.A. = (85 + 45 + 55 + 79) ÷ 4 = 66
2nd M.A. = (45 + 55 + 79 + 96) ÷ 4 = 68.75
Remaining M.A.s: 69.25, 70, 71, 70.5, 71.75, 72, 73.5

d The charges are slowly increasing.

---

1 Check the moving averages then re-plot the graph.
2 Use the seasonal variation to estimate the charge for Q1 of 2002. Plot this on the same graph.
3 Use your point to calculate then plot the next moving average.
4 Does your estimate fit the trend?

TEST

Averages from frequency tables (1)

● Finding the median, mode, range

The frequency table shows the number of pets owned by 19 people.

No. of pets	Frequency
0	2
1	6
2	4
3	7
Total	19

The first 2 people have 0 pets, the next 6 have 1 pet, ...

The median is the number of pets owned by the 10th person. Median = 2 pets

The mode is the number of pets with the highest frequency. Mode = 3 pets

Range = 3 – 0 = 3 pets

● Finding the mean

➤ Q & A

Find the mean number of cars per household.

No. of cars	Frequency
0	6
1	11
2	29
3	4

Answer

Add an extra column to the table to record the 'No. of cars × Frequency'.

No. of cars	Frequency	No. of cars × Freq.
0	6	0
1	11	11
2	29	58
3	4	12
Totals	50	81

$0 \times 6 = 0$

29 houses have 2 cars. That's $2 \times 29 = 58$ cars.

There are 81 cars at the 50 houses.

Mean = 81 ÷ 50 = 1.62 cars per household

Look at the 'No. of pets' table above.

1 Calculate the mean number of pets.

Look at the 'No. of cars' table in the **Q & A**.

2 What is the median number of cars per household?

3 What is the modal number of cars?

TEST

Averages from frequency tables (2)

● Estimating the mean from grouped data
You don't have the raw data, so you can only <u>estimate</u> the mean.

➤ Q & A
The table shows the lengths of candles on a birthday cake.
Estimate the mean length.

Answer

➤ Method
❶ Add a <u>column of midpoints</u>.
❷ <u>Multiply</u> each <u>midpoint</u> by its <u>frequency</u>.
❸ <u>Total</u> this column.
❹ <u>Divide</u> by the <u>total frequency</u>.

Length (L mm)	Frequency	Midpoint	Freq. × midpoint
$80 \leqslant L < 90$	2	85	170
$90 \leqslant L < 100$	2	95	190
$100 \leqslant L < 110$	3	105	315
$110 \leqslant L < 120$	6	115	690
$120 \leqslant L < 130$	3	125	375
Total	16	Total	1740

Estimated mean = 1740 ÷ 16 = <u>109 mm</u> (to nearest mm)

● Which group contains the median?
The median is between the 8th and 9th values, so it's in the $110 \leqslant L < 120$ group.

● Finding the modal group
$110 \leqslant L < 120$ has the <u>highest frequency</u> so it's the <u>modal group</u>.

● Estimating the range
Using the midpoints, estimated range = 125 − 85 = 40 mm.

These are the heights (h cm) of 20 students:
152, 167, 169, 158, 177, 165, 172, 168, 156, 161,
163, 166, 171, 157, 162, 169, 168, 155, 176, 167

a Put the data into a frequency table with groups
$150 \leqslant h < 155$, $155 \leqslant h < 160$, ... (Use tallies to help you.)
b Use the table to calculate an estimate for the mean.
c Which group is the median in? **d** Which is the modal group?

TEST

Frequency diagrams (1)

● Histograms

In a <u>bar chart</u> the <u>height</u> of the bar represents <u>frequency</u>.
In a <u>histogram</u>, it is the <u>area</u> that represents <u>frequency</u>.

● Frequency density

You need to learn this formula:

> Frequency density = Frequency ÷ Group width

➤ Q & A

The table shows the ages of some TVs.
Draw a histogram to represent the data.

Age (months)	Frequency
0–	6
12–	15
18–	12
24–60	9

Answer

Add two extra columns to the table for
'Group width' and 'Frequency density'.

Age (months)	Frequency	Group width	Frequency density
0–	6	12	6 ÷ 12 = 0.5
12–	15	6	15 ÷ 6 = 2.5
18–	12	6	12 ÷ 6 = 2
24–60	9	36	9 ÷ 36 = 0.25

Draw the histogram with 'Frequency density' on the vertical axis.

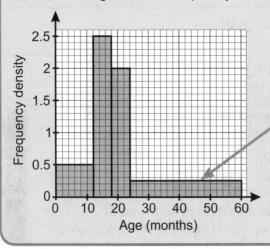

This bar is for the 24–60 group. It is 0.25 tall because the frequency density is 0.25.

Frequency diagrams (2)

● Reading frequencies off histograms

➤ Q & A

The histogram shows heights of a selection of plants.
How many plants were 10 to 15 cm?

Answer

> ### ➤ Method
> ❶ <u>Read off</u> the frequency density.
> ❷ <u>Multiply</u> by the group width.

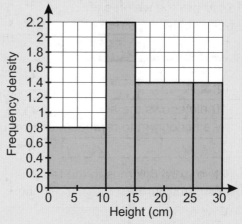

Frequency density = 2.2
Group width = 5
So Frequency = 2.2 × 5 = <u>11</u>

● Frequency polygons

A frequency polygon can be drawn on top of a histogram by joining the tops of the bars.

(Or you could just draw one by plotting frequency or frequency density against mid-interval value.)

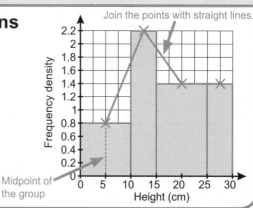

Join the points with straight lines.

Midpoint of the group

---

1 The table shows how far a group of people travel to work.

Distance (miles)	0–	5–	10–	20–30
Frequency	10	18	16	8

   a Draw a histogram for this data.
   b Draw a frequency polygon for this data.

2 Look at the **Q & A** on this page. Find the other frequencies.

TEST

Cumulative frequency (1)

The <u>cumulative frequency</u> (C.F.) is the <u>running total</u> of frequency up to the <u>end of the group</u>. You always plot it at the <u>end of the group</u>.

➤ Q & A

These are the weights of wheelie bins in a street.

Weight (W kg)	Frequency
$0 \leqslant W < 5$	5
$5 \leqslant W < 10$	12
$10 \leqslant W < 15$	27
$15 \leqslant W < 20$	14
$20 \leqslant W < 25$	2

Draw a cumulative frequency diagram.

Answer

Add a 3rd column to the table to work out the C.F.s:

Cumulative frequency
5
5 + 12 = 17
17 + 27 = 44
44 + 14 = 58
58 + 2 = 60

Think of cumulative frequency as the '<u>running total</u>'.

➤ Method

❶ Calculate the <u>C.F.s</u>.
❷ Draw a <u>horizontal axis</u> for the <u>end-points</u> of the groups. Draw a <u>vertical axis</u> for <u>C.F.</u>
❸ Plot each <u>C.F.</u> against the group <u>end-point</u>.
❹ Join the points with a <u>smooth curve</u>.

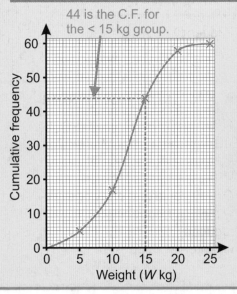

44 is the C.F. for the < 15 kg group.

● Reading from the graph

You can use the graph to find out how many wheelie bins weigh more or less than a particular weight.

Check this on the graph by drawing a line up from 18 kg to the curve. Then draw a line across to the cumulative frequency axis. Go on!

➤ Example

The C.F. for 18 kg is 54. This means that 54 bins weigh less than 18 kg.

Cumulative frequency (2)

● Median, quartiles & interquartile range

The <u>median</u> is <u>halfway</u> through the distribution.

The <u>lower quartile</u> (LQ) is a <u>quarter of the way</u> through.

The <u>upper quartile</u> (UQ) is <u>three-quarters of the way</u> through.

> Interquartile range (IQR) = upper quartile − lower quartile

➤ Q & A

Use the cumulative frequency graph to find

a the median

b the interquartile range.

Answer

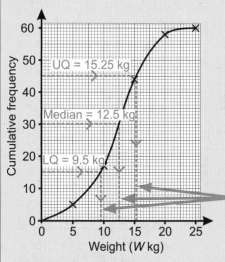

➤ Method

❶ <u>Decide how far up</u> the C.F. axis you need to go: <u>halfway</u> for the median, a <u>quarter</u> of the way for the LQ, <u>three-quarters</u> of the way for the UQ.

❷ Draw a <u>horizontal line</u> to the C.F. curve.

❸ Draw a <u>vertical line</u> down to the other axis.

❹ <u>Read off</u> the value.

The total C.F. is 60, so the <u>median</u> has C.F. = 60 ÷ 2 = <u>30</u>, the <u>LQ</u> has C.F. = 60 ÷ 4 = <u>15</u>, the <u>UQ</u> has C.F. = 60 ÷ 4 × 3 = <u>45</u>.

Now, read off the values for the median, UQ and LQ from the graph.

a Median = <u>12.5 kg</u>   **b** IQR = UQ − LQ = 15.25 − 9.5 = <u>5.75 kg</u>

Plot the cumulative frequency curve for these TV prices. Use it to find the median, lower and upper quartiles, and the interquartile range.

TV price (£P)	150–	200–	250–	300–	350–
Frequency	3	8	12	6	1

TEST

Box plots

If you have drawn a cumulative frequency diagram, you can draw a
<u>box plot</u> (sometimes called a <u>box and whisker diagram</u>) underneath.

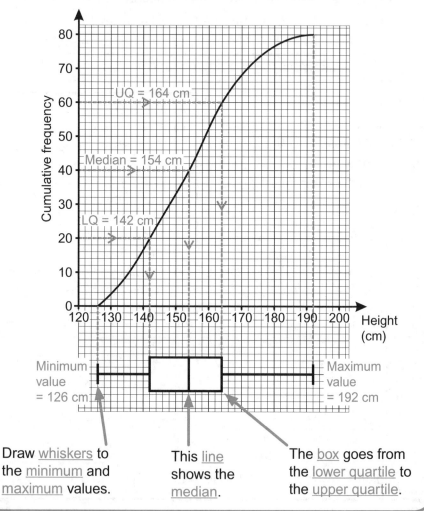

Draw <u>whiskers</u> to
the <u>minimum</u> and
<u>maximum</u> values.

This <u>line</u>
shows the
<u>median</u>.

The <u>box</u> goes from
the <u>lower quartile</u> to
the <u>upper quartile</u>.

Look at this box plot.
Write down the minimum,
maximum, lower quartile,
upper quartile and median.

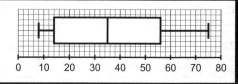

TEST

Speedy Revision

Comparing sets of data

● Comparing box plots

These box plots show some girls' and boys' exam marks.

On average, the girls got <u>higher marks</u> than the boys (<u>higher median</u>).

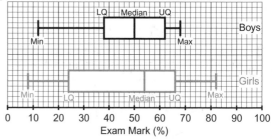

The <u>range</u> (min to max) and <u>interquartile range</u> (LQ to UQ) are bigger for the girls, so there is <u>more variation</u> in the girls' marks.

● Comparing histograms

These histograms show the heights of two varieties of daffodil.

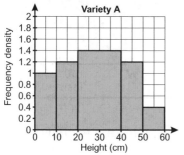
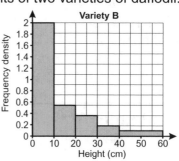

Variety A has a <u>larger spread</u> (or <u>wider dispersion</u>) than variety B. (Histogram A has lots of quite tall bars, whereas B has one bar much taller than the rest).

Histogram B is '<u>positively skewed</u>' (most plants are 0–10 cm tall, but a few plants are taller than this). Histogram A is <u>fairly symmetrical</u>.

Here is the histogram for a third variety of daffodil.

Use this histogram and the histogram above to compare varieties B and C.

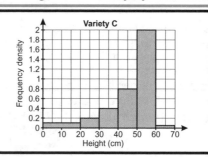

TEST

Scatter graphs

● Plotting scatter graphs

This table shows some students' results for two maths tests.

Test 1	5	8	9	11	15	17	19
Test 2	5	9	12	14	16	18	20

You can <u>plot the points</u> on a graph – this is a <u>scatter graph</u>.

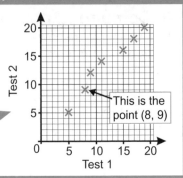

This is the point (8, 9)

● Line of best fit

This is a line drawn on a <u>scatter graph</u> that shows the <u>general direction</u> of the points.

You should try to get the <u>same</u> number of points <u>above</u> the line as <u>below</u>.

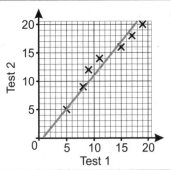

● Correlation

This is a fancy way of saying whether the points are related or not:

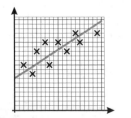

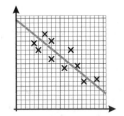

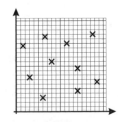

Positive correlation (/)
<u>Strong</u> if the points lie <u>close to a straight line</u>, otherwise <u>weak</u>.

Negative correlation (\)
<u>Strong</u> if the points lie <u>close to a straight line</u>, otherwise <u>weak</u>.

No correlation
The points seem to be <u>randomly</u> positioned.

Show the data as a scatter diagram.
Describe the correlation.

Age (years)	1	6	4	4	10	3	8	7	9
Value (£)	45	18	28	24	4	37	10	17	9

TEST

Probability (1)

<u>Probabilities</u> can be given as <u>fractions or decimals</u>, but they are always <u>between 0 and 1</u>. If something has probability <u>0 it can't happen</u>; if it has probability <u>1 it will definitely happen</u>.

● Theoretical probability

$$P(\text{event}) = \frac{\text{No. of ways event can occur}}{\text{No. of possible outcomes}}$$

<u>P(event)</u> is a short way of writing '<u>the probability of an event happening</u>'.

> **Example**
> If an ordinary dice is rolled:
> $P(6) = \frac{1}{6}$
> $P(\text{even}) = \frac{3}{6} = \frac{1}{2}$

● Mutually exclusive

Outcomes are <u>mutually exclusive</u> if they <u>can't happen at the same time</u>.

> **Example**
> You can't get a head *and* a tail when you toss a coin.

Learn these important rules for mutually exclusive events:

❶ P(Not A) = 1 – P(A) ❷ P(A or B) = P(A) + P(B)

➤ Q & A

There are 6 blue, 4 yellow, 3 black and 2 green beads in a bag.
A bead is picked at random. What is the probability that it is
a blue **b** yellow **c** not blue **d** blue or yellow?

Answer

a $P(\text{blue}) = \frac{6}{15} = \frac{2}{5}$

b $P(\text{yellow}) = \frac{4}{15}$

c $P(\text{not blue}) = 1 - P(\text{blue}) = 1 - \frac{2}{5} = \frac{3}{5}$

d $P(\text{blue or yellow}) = P(\text{blue}) + P(\text{yellow}) = \frac{6}{15} + \frac{4}{15} = \frac{10}{15} = \frac{2}{3}$

Probability (2)

● Experimental probability

You can carry out trials to estimate probability, e.g. rolling a dice lots of times.

$$\text{Estimated probability} = \frac{\text{Number of successful trials}}{\text{Total number of trials}}$$

The more trials, the better the estimate.

> Estimated probability is sometimes called 'relative frequency'.

➤ Q & A

Here are the results of rolling a dice 100 times.

Number	1	2	3	4	5	6
Frequency	16	17	20	13	15	19

Estimate the probability of getting a 5.

Answer

$P(5) = \frac{15}{100} = \frac{3}{20}$

➤ Method

❶ Use the formula to calculate the probability.

❷ Simplify if possible.

● Independent events

If you roll a fair dice twice, the number you get the first time doesn't affect the number you get the second time. These are independent events.

For independent events A and B: | $P(A \text{ and } B) = P(A) \times P(B)$

➤ Q & A

A coin is tossed twice. Use a tree diagram to find the probability of getting two heads.

Answer

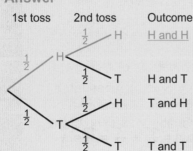

1st toss	2nd toss	Outcome

➤ Method

❶ Put outcomes and probabilities on the tree diagram.

❷ Pick out the required outcome.

❸ Multiply along the branches.

$P(H \text{ and } H) = P(H) \times P(H)$

$= \frac{1}{2} \times \frac{1}{2} = \frac{1}{4}$

Probability (3)

● Without replacement

Sometimes, even though the events and outcomes seem the same, the probabilities will change. Look out for the words 'without replacement' or more than one thing being picked at the same time.

➤ Q & A

A bag contains 6 green beads and 4 red beads. If you pick two beads without replacement, what is the probability that one is red and one is green?

The probability of picking a moose is zero...

Answer

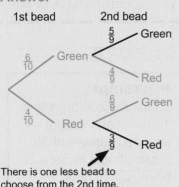

1st bead   2nd bead

$\frac{5}{9}$ Green

$\frac{6}{10}$ Green

$\frac{4}{9}$ Red

$\frac{6}{9}$ Green

$\frac{4}{10}$ Red

$\frac{3}{9}$ Red

There is one less bead to choose from the 2nd time.

P(Green and Red) = $\frac{6}{10} \times \frac{4}{9} = \frac{4}{15}$

P(Red and Green) = $\frac{4}{10} \times \frac{6}{9} = \frac{4}{15}$

There are two ways, so use the OR rule and add probabilities.

Total probability = $\frac{4}{15} + \frac{4}{15} = \frac{8}{15}$

---

1 Two dice are rolled and the scores multiplied. Find the probability of getting an even product. (Hint: draw a table.)

2 A card is picked at random from an ordinary pack of cards. What is the probability that it is
   a a Spade   **b** not a King
   c a red card or the Ace of Spades?

3 Two fair dice are rolled. What's the probability of a double 6?

4 Three of Kyle's five friends are hungry. Kyle only has three biscuits. He gives the biscuits to his friends at random (no more than one each). What is the probability that two of the hungry friends get a biscuit?

TEST

Surveys & sampling

● Primary & secondary data

Data you <u>collect yourself</u> is called <u>primary data</u>.
<u>Secondary data already exists</u>, e.g. in a newspaper or on the Internet.

● Questionnaires

Ask <u>simple questions</u> with a <u>clear choice of answers</u>.
<u>Bad questions</u> are either <u>too vague</u>, <u>too personal</u> or they <u>influence the answer</u>. For example, anything that starts 'Do you agree...' pushes people to say 'Yes'. <u>Leading questions</u> introduce <u>bias</u>.

● Pilot surveys

Always test a questionnaire by doing a '<u>pilot survey</u>'. This means trying it on a few people to see whether your questions work or not.

● Sampling

<u>Random sampling:</u> Each member of the population has an equal chance of being picked.

<u>Stratified sampling:</u> The population is divided into groups (strata), and a random sample is taken from each group. Samples must be in the same proportion as the original groups.

> ➤ **Example**
> There are 200 boys and 100 girls at a school. A stratified sample of 30 pupils should include 20 boys and 10 girls.

<u>Selective (systematic) sampling:</u>
For a 20% selective sample (i.e. 1 in 5), pick one of the first 5 members at random, then every 5th member after that. This is a good way of testing, say, lightbulbs coming off a production line.

---

1 Explain why these are not suitable for a questionnaire.
  a Do you eat chips... sometimes? often? never?
  b Have you broken the law? Yes/No
  c Isn't it best to buy quality brands? Yes/No

2 1000 pupils attend Metherton School.
  a Explain how you could take a random sample of 50 pupils.
  600 of the pupils are at Key Stage 3. 400 are at Key Stage 4.
  b Explain how to take a stratified sample of 50 pupils.

TEST

Speedy revision test (1)

These questions test the basic facts. The simple truth is that the more of them you can answer, the better you'll do in your exams. So try them as often as you can. (The answers can be found on the pages given at the end of each question.)

1 What are the first five square, cube and triangular numbers? (p6)

2 Write down the nth terms of the powers of 2, powers of 10, and those in **1**. (p6)

3 What are the first seven prime numbers? (p7)

4 What is 60 expressed as a product of its prime factors? (p8)

5 How do you find the LCM of two numbers? What about the HCF? (p9)

6 How do you divide a fraction by a fraction? (p11)

7 What are the 9 fraction/decimal/percentage equivalents you should know? (p12)

8 How do you convert a fraction to a percentage? (p13)

9 How can you tell if a fraction will give a terminating decimal? (p14)

10 Convert 0.3636... to a fraction. (p14)

11 What are the two rules for multiplying and dividing negative numbers? (p15)

12 What is any non-zero number to the power of zero? (p16)

13 What is any number to the power of one? (p16)

14 What is six to the power of minus one? (p16)

15 Complete: To multiply powers of the same number you _____ the indices.
       To divide powers of the same number you _____ the indices.
       To take the power of a power you _____ the indices. (p17)

16 Work out the value of 8 to the power of two-thirds. (p17)

17 What is a rational number? What is an irrational number? (p18)

18 What are the two important rules for multiplying and dividing surds? (p18)

19 How would you simplify a fraction with a surd in the denominator? (p19)

20 What does BIDMAS stand for? (p20)

21 What is the formula for 'Percentage change'? (p22)

22 Divide £120 in the ratio 2 : 3. (p24)

23 Round: **a** 0.168 to 2 decimal places **b** 5384 to 2 significant figures. (p26–27)

24 Estimate the value of $(11.6 \times \sqrt{8.8}) \div (1.8^3 + 7.43)$. (p27)

25 Work out **a** $(6 \times 10^5) \times (2 \times 10^4)$ **b** $(2.5 \times 10^5) + (3.4 \times 10^4)$. (p29–30)

26 Explain what these are: term, expression, equation, formula. (p31)

27 When multiplying out double brackets, what should you draw? (p32)

28 What does 'factorising' mean? (p32)

29 What should you do first when answering a trial & improvement question? (p36)

30 How do you work out the midpoint of a line between two points? (p37)

31 How do you work out the gradient of a line? (p39)

32 How do you know if the gradient is positive or negative? (p39)

33 In '$y = mx + c$', what do m and c tell you? (p40)

34 What is the product of the gradients of perpendicular lines? (p41)

35 When showing inequalities on a graph, what does a broken line mean? (p43)

36 What is the equation of a circle? (p44)

37 Why is there no excuse for getting simultaneous equations wrong? (p48)

38 Factorise **a** $x^2 + 3x - 10$ **b** $2x^2 - x - 15$ **c** $x^2 - a^2$. (p49–50)

39 Use the quadratic formula to solve $4x^2 + 6x - 5 = 0$ to 1 dp. (p51)

Speedy revision test (2)

40 Solve $x^2 - 2x - 4 = 0$ by completing the square. Answer in surd form. (p51)
41 Sketch: **a** $y = -x$ **b** $y = 2x$ **c** $y = x^2$ **d** $y = -x^2$ **e** $y = x^3$ **f** $y = 2^x$ **g** $y = \frac{1}{x}$ (p54)
42 Sketch the graphs of $y = \sin x$, $y = \cos x$ and $y = \tan x$. (p55)
43 What are the 4 types of graph transformation, and how do they work? (p56–57)
44 What does the gradient give in a distance–time graph? velocity–time? (p58)
45 State the 4 basic cases of direct/inverse proportion you are likely to meet. (p60)
46 The difference between consecutive terms in a linear sequence is what? (p61)
47 What is the order of rotation symmetry of a parallelogram? (p63)
48 Sketch diagrams to show: **a** vertically opposite angles **b** alternate angles
   c corresponding angles **d** supplementary angles. (p64)
49 What are the two formulae concerning interior and exterior angles? (p65)
50 Give the area formulae for a triangle, rectangle, parallelogram, trapezium. (p66)
51 What's the formula for the circumference of a circle? How about the area? (p67)
52 Draw a circle and label these: chord, tangent, arc, sector, segment. (p67)
53 Give the volume formulae for a cuboid, prism, pyramid. (p69)
54 Give the volume and surface area formulae for a cylinder, cone, sphere. (p69)
55 How do you know if an expression is a length, area or volume? (p73)
56 What is Pythagoras' theorem? (p74)
57 What are the formulae for sin, cos and tan (in right-angled triangles)? (p76)
58 Write down the sine rule and the cosine rule. (p79)
59 What are the two situations when you should use the cosine rule? (p79–80)
60 What are the three things you should know about bearings? (p82)
61 Give the metric to imperial conversions for length, mass and capacity. (p83)
62 A is 162 cm tall. T is 158 cm tall. What is the minimum difference? (p85)
63 Sketch the formula triangles for speed and density. (p86)
64 State the 8 circle theorems, including diagrams. Then prove the last 5. (p87–89)
65 What are the four loci that you should know? Draw accurate diagrams. (p91)
66 The lengths in a shape are enlarged by a scale factor k. What happens to the area? What happens to the volume? (p93)
67 What are the four conditions for congruent triangles? (p93)
68 Look at the **Q & A** on page 95. What is $\overrightarrow{QM}$? (p95, answer at bottom of page)
69 How are these defined: translation, reflection, rotation, enlargement? (p96–98)
70 How do you work out the mode, median, mean and range? (p100)
71 How do you estimate the mean from a grouped frequency table? (p105)
72 What is the formula for frequency density? (p106)
73 Joining the middle of the tops of the bars in a histogram gives what? (p107)
74 How do you find the interquartile range from a cumulative frequency curve? (p109)
75 What are the five things that a box plot shows? (p110)
76 Draw diagrams to show positive, negative and no linear correlation. (p112)
77 What is the formula used to work out theoretical probability? (p113)
78 If A and B are mutually exclusive what are P(Not A) and P(A or B)? (p113)
79 What is the formula used to work out experimental probability? (p114)
80 If A and B are independent events, what is P(A and B)? (p114)
81 What are the three methods of sampling? (p116)

TEST answers

Page 4 Non-calculator tricks
1 **a** 562 181.3 **b** 56 218 130 **c** 562 181 300
2 **a** 30.0218 **b** 0.030 021 8
3 **a** 1169 **b** 1900 **c** 120 **d** 1.6 **e** 3080

Page 5 Written multiplication & division
a 44.94 **b** 155.04 **c** 13.4 **d** 21.6

Page 6 Special number sequences
1 **a** 1, 4, 9, 16, 25, 36, 49, 64, 81, 100
  b 1, 8, 27, 64, 125, 216, 343, 512, 729, 1000
  c 1, 3, 6, 10, 15, 21, 28, 36, 45, 55
2 **a** 2, 4, 8, 16, 32, 64, 128, 256, 512, 1024
  b 10, 100, 1000, 10 000, 100 000, 1 000 000, 10 000 000, 100 000 000, 1 000 000 000, 10 000 000 000
3 **a** $2n$ **b** $2n - 1$ (see p61 if not sure)
4 Check yourself by looking at page 6.

Page 7 Prime numbers
1 2, 3, 5, 7, 11, 13, 17, 19, 23, 29, 31, 37, 41, 43, 47
2 **a** No **b** No (both are multiples of 2)
  c No (multiple of 5)
3 All are multiples of 3, so not prime.

Page 8 Multiples, factors & prime factorisation
1 **a** 7, 14, 21, 28, 35
  b 12, 24, 36, 48, 60
  c 21, 42, 63, 84, 105
  d 104, 208, 312, 416, 520
2 **a** 1, 2, 3, 4, 6, 8, 12, 24
  b 1, 2, 4, 7, 8, 14, 28, 56
  c 1, 2, 7, 14, 49, 98
3 **a** 2^6 **b** 3^4 **c** $2^3 \times 3 \times 19$ **d** $5^2 \times 7^2$
  e $2 \times 3 \times 5 \times 7 \times 11$

Page 9 LCM & HCF
1 **a** $2 \times 2 \times 2 \times 2 \times 3 \times 3 = 144$
  b $2 \times 5 \times 5 \times 19 = 950$
2 **a** $2 \times 2 \times 3 = 12$ **b** $2 \times 2 = 4$
3 LCM $= 2 \times 2 \times 2 \times 3 \times 7 = 168$, HCF $= 2$

Page 11 Fractions (2)
1 **a** $\frac{2}{3}$ **b** $\frac{1}{4}$ **c** $\frac{7}{10}$ **d** $\frac{1}{24}$ **e** $\frac{45}{56}$
  f $\frac{5}{28}$ **g** $1\frac{3}{5}$ **h** $\frac{1}{4}$ **i** $1\frac{1}{2}$ **j** $\frac{5}{24}$
2 **a** $\frac{16}{5}$ **b** $\frac{35}{8}$
3 **a** $8\frac{1}{5}$ **b** $7\frac{5}{8}$
4 **a** £33 **b** £45 **c** 9300 kg

Page 13 Fractions, decimals & percentages (2)
1 **a** 0.375 **b** 0.3 **c** 0.104
2 **a** $\frac{3}{5}$ **b** $\frac{3}{20}$ **c** $\frac{153}{1000}$
3 **a** 0.35 **b** 0.57 **c** 0.08
4 **a** 45% **b** 67% **c** 30%
5 **a** 60% **b** 12% **c** 65%
6 **a** $\frac{21}{100}$ **b** $\frac{1}{20}$ **c** $\frac{7}{20}$
7 145%, 3.45, $4\frac{1}{8}$, 4.2

Page 14 Terminating & recurring decimals
1 Yes $(20 = 2^2 \times 5)$
2 **a** $0.\dot{6}$ **b** $0.3\dot{6}$ **c** $0.\dot{1}4285\dot{7}$
3 **a** $\frac{4}{9}$ **b** $\frac{546}{999} = \frac{182}{333}$ **c** $\frac{457}{990}$

Page 15 Negative numbers
1 $-5, -4, 0, 2, 3$
2 **a** -3 **b** -26 **c** 20 **d** -4 **e** 30 **f** -144

Page 17 Powers & roots (2)
1 **a** 64 **b** 7 **c** $\frac{1}{25}$ **d** 1 **e** 32 **f** $\frac{1}{16}$
2 **a** 6 (or -6) **b** 8 (or -8) **c** 13 (or -13)
  d 10 **e** 7 **f** 3
3 **a** 7^7 **b** 2^5 **c** 5^{24} 4 81

Page 19 Rational, irrational & surds (2)
1 **b**, **c** and **f** are irrational, others are rational
2 **a** 4 **b** $6\sqrt{5}$ **c** $\frac{9\sqrt{5}}{20}$ **d** $7 + \sqrt{5}$

Page 20 BIDMAS & bracket buttons
a 198 **b** 169 **c** $\frac{5}{7}$ **d** 176

Page 23 Percentages (3)
1 **a** 37.5 g **b** 212.5 g   2 £20
3 Price without VAT is £80   4 12.5%
5 £70 246.40   6 £386.97

Page 25 Ratio & proportion (2)
1 **a** $1 : 6$ **b** $9 : 5$ **c** $35 : 3$
2 240 ml : 560 ml   3 **a** 15 cm **b** 8 cm
4 The 350 g jar is better value (0.797p per gram against 0.895p per gram for the 200 g jar).
5 £6.75   6 3 hours 45 minutes

Page 27 Rounding & estimating (2)
1 0.58, 0.02, 12.88   2 350, 1.0, 0.81
3 **a** 5 **b** 1200   4 **a** 5.78 **b** 1273.87

Page 28 Standard index form (1)
a 3.45×10^2 **b** 2.4×10^{-4} **c** 4.5×10^4
d 7.64×10^8 **e** 2.453×10^{-6} **f** 1.0×10^7

Page 29 Standard index form (2)
a 3700 **b** 0.000 44 **c** 5 430 000
d 0.000 001 2

Answers

TEST answers

Page 30 Standard index form (3)
1 **a** 2×10^{10} **b** 8.2×10^7 **c** 2×10^3
  d 2×10 **e** 2.4×10^5 **f** 7.64×10^4
  g 4×10^{-3} **h** 8.13×10^7

Page 31 Using letters
a Term (or single-term expression)
b Expression **c** Formula **d** Equation

Page 32 Simplifying expressions (2)
1 **a** $6a$ **b** $3x^2 + 5x$ **c** $9x - 19y$ **d** $p^2 - 2p + 4$
2 **a** $x^2 + 9x + 20$ **b** $2x^2 - 4x - 6$
  c $4y^2 - 18y + 18$

Page 32 Factorising expressions
1 **a** $2(3y - 1)$ **b** $r(s + 1)$
  c $2y(9y - 2)$ **d** $s(12r^2 + 3r - 4)$
2 $\dfrac{5x(x - 4)}{x^2(x - 4)} = \dfrac{5}{x}$

Page 33 Formulae
1 $C = 10 - 1.5p$ 2 £320
3 **a** 13 **b** −16   4 **a** 31 **b** 54

Page 34 Rearranging formulae
1 **a** $q = \dfrac{\sqrt{p}}{2}$ **b** $q = \dfrac{\sqrt{p}}{9}$
2 **a** $a = 1 - 3b$ **b** $a = \dfrac{5b + 4}{1 - b}$

Page 35 Solving equations
1 $g = 1$ 2 $y = 3$
3 $p = -11$ 4 **a** $m = 8$ **b** $n = 4$

Page 36 Trial & improvement
1 $x = 3.77$ 2 2.3

Page 37 Coordinates
1 A(0, 0, 2), B(0, 3, 2), C(4, 3, 2), D(4, 0, 2)
  E(0, 0, 0), F(0, 3, 0), G(4, 3, 0), H(4, 0, 0)
2 (4, 6)

Page 38 Straight-line graphs (1)
a

x	−2	−1	0	1	2
$y = 3x + 2$	−4	−1	2	5	8

b
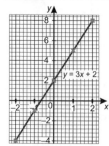

Page 41 Straight line graphs (4)
1
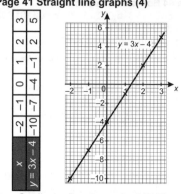

2 **a** Gradient = 3, cuts y-axis at (0, 5)
  b Gradient = 2, cuts y-axis at (0, −1)
3 **a** $y = -4x - 2$ **b** $y = \frac{1}{4}x - 2$
4 **a** $y = 2x$ **b** $y = -2x + 6$ **c** $y = x + 2$

Pages 43 Inequalities (2)
1 **a** −4, −3, −2, −1, 0, 1
  b
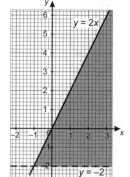

2 **a** $x < 2$ **b**

3
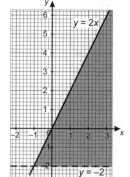

4 **a** $y \leqslant 2$ **b**
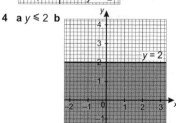

Speedy Revision

TEST answers

Page 44 Equation of a circle

1

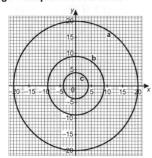

2 $x^2 + y^2 = 6.25$

Page 45 Simultaneous equations (1)

1 $x = 4, y = 1$

2 $x = 1, y = -1$

3 Their graphs are parallel, so they do not cross.

Page 46 Simultaneous equations (2)

a $x = -0.3, y = -5$ or $x = 2.7, y = 4.2$

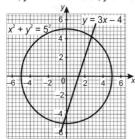

b $x = -2.6, y = 5.6$ or $x = -0.4, y = 3.4$

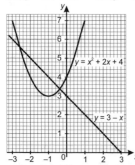

Page 47 Simultaneous equations (3)

1 $x = 5, y = 4$

2 $x = -2, y = 2$

Page 48 Simultaneous equations (4)

1 **a** $x = 2.4, y = 4.2$
   b $x = -3, y = -4$ or $x = 4, y = 3$
   c $x = -1, y = 0$ or $x = 0.5, y = 4.5$
2 Their graphs do not intersect.

Page 50 Quadratics (2)

1 **a** $(x + 1)(x + 6)$ **b** $(x - 1)(x - 10)$
   c $(x + 3)(x - 5)$
2 **a** $(2x - 1)(x - 4)$ **b** $2(3x + 2)(x + 1)$
   c $(4x - 5)(x + 3)$
3 **a** $(x + 6)(x - 6)$ **b** $(3x + 7)(3x - 7)$
   c $4(p + 2q)(p - 2q)$
4 **a** $x = 1$ or 4 **b** $x = -4$ or 4 **c** $x = -3$ or -2
   d $x = -2$ or 2 **e** $x = \frac{1}{5}$ or 3 **f** $x = -4$ or -3

Page 51 Quadratics (3)

a $x = -3.6$ or 0.6 **b** $x = -0.3$ or 9.3

Page 52 Quadratics (4)

x	-3	-2	-1	0	1	2	3
$y = x^2 - x - 4$	8	2	-2	-4	-4	-2	2

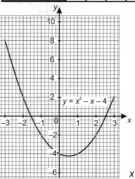

$x = -1.6$ or 2.6

Page 53 Quadratics (5)

1 $x = 0.4$ or 2.6

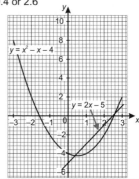

TEST answers

2 $x < -1.6$ or $x > 2.6$

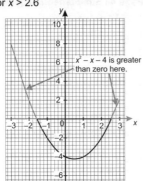

$x^2 - x - 4$ is greater than zero here.

Page 55 Graphs you should know (2)

a–c

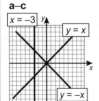

d–e

f–g

h

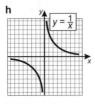

i

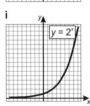

j–l Check these carefully against the graphs on page 55.

Page 57 Graph transformations (2)

1 a Shift graph up 3 **b** Shift graph right 2

c–d

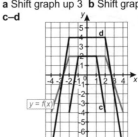

2 a Shift $y = \cos x$ right 180° so it goes through (180, 1)

b Shift $y = x^3$ up 4

c Shift $y = x^3$ left 4

d–e

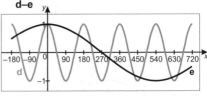

f Stretch $y = \sin x$ so y goes from -3 to 3

Page 59 Real-life graphs (2)

1 a 160 km **b** 32 km/h

2 a During the seventh minute, 6 m/s

b 5 m/s ÷ 60 s = 0.08 m/s²

c Deceleration of 0.05 m/s² (or −0.05 m/s²)

3

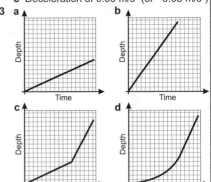

Page 60 Direct & inverse proportion

1 43.12 ($s = 5.5t^2$)

2 25 cm ($F = \dfrac{40\,000}{d^2}$)

TEST answers

Page 61 Sequences
a 14, $3n - 1$, 299 b -10, $15 - 5n$, -485
c 24, $n^2 - 1$, 9999

Page 63 Symmetry & properties of shapes (2)
1 a i 2 ii 2 b i 1 ii 1 c i 3 ii 3
2 For example:

Page 64 Angles & parallel lines
$a = 65°$, $b = 56°$, $c = 124°$, $d = 124°$,
$e = 38°$, $f = 128°$, $g = 128°$, $h = 52°$

Page 65 Polygons
1 a Interior = 90°, Exterior = 90°
   b Interior = 120°, Exterior = 60°
   c Interior = 144°, Exterior = 36°
2 72 sides

Page 66 Areas of triangles & quadrilaterals
a 42 cm² b 1.8 km² c 18 cm² d 70 m²

Page 67 Circles
1 a 18.8 cm b 28.3 cm²
2 a 3.14 cm b 4.71 cm²
3 $0.36\pi - 0.72$ m²

Page 68 Composite shapes
a i 40 cm ii 75 cm²
b i 3.14 m ii 0.339 m²

Page 72 Volume & surface area (4)
1 a 600 m³ b 216 cm³ c 12.6 m³
2 a 152.4 m² b 138.5 cm² (use Pythagoras to find l with 3.5 cm for r) c 980 cm²
3 6×10^8 cm³, 0.01385 m²

Page 73 Dimensions
a Area b None (volume + number) c Area
d None (π is a number) e Length f Volume

Page 75 Pythagoras' theorem (2)
1 a 12.5 cm b 12.1 cm c 19.6 km
2 a 10.6 units b 19.2 units

Page 77 Trigonometry (2)
1 a 31.0° (tan) b 7.5 cm (cos) c 13 cm (sin)
2 19.6 m (tan)

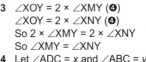

Page 78 Trigonometry (3)
1 −290°, −70°, 70°, 290°
2 41.8°, 138.2°, 401.8°, 498.2°
3 −315°, −135°, 45°, 225°

Page 80 Sine & cosine rules (2)
a 108.2° (cosine) b 2.5 cm (cosine)
c 24.5° (sine) d 3.1 cm (sine)

Page 81 3-D Pythagoras & trigonometry
a 5.1 m b 5.9 m c 59° d 9.7°

Page 82 Bearings
1 333°
2 323° (use tan, subtract from 360°)

Page 83 Converting between measures
1 a 42 lb b 0.35 litre
2 a About 1.5 ft b About 90 litres

Page 84 Rounding measures
a 42.5 hours, 43.5 hours
b 26.5 pints, 27.5 pints
c 2.75 cm, 2.85 cm
d 9.15 litres, 9.25 litres

Page 85 Calculating with rounded measures
1 56.6 mm (14.15 mm × 4)
2 6.93 m/s (100.5 m ÷ 14.5 s)

Page 86 Compound measures
1 40 minutes 2 1000 kg

Page 88 Circle theorems (2)
a 68° (isosceles triangle)
b 22° (tangent and radius at right angles)
c 59° (angle at circumference of semicircle)
d 59° (angles in same segment)
e 49° (opposite angles, alternate segment theorem)
f 56° (angles at centre and circumference)
g 124° (cyclic quadrilateral)

Page 89 Circle theorems (3)
1 See Q & A on page 89.
2 $\angle AOB = 180°$ (straight line)
   $\angle AOB = 2 \times \angle APB$ (❹)
   So $2 \times \angle APB = 180°$
   So $\angle APB = 90°$
3 $\angle XOY = 2 \times \angle XMY$ (❹)
   $\angle XOY = 2 \times \angle XNY$ (❹)
   So $2 \times \angle XMY = 2 \times \angle XNY$
   So $\angle XMY = \angle XNY$
4 Let $\angle ADC = x$ and $\angle ABC = y$
   Then obtuse $\angle AOC = 2 \times \angle ADC = 2x$ (❹)
   And reflex $\angle AOC = 2 \times \angle ABC = 2y$ (❹)
   But obtuse $\angle AOC$ + reflex $\angle AOC = 360°$ (angles at a point)
   So $2x + 2y = 360°$
   Therefore $x + y = 180°$
   i.e. $\angle ADC + \angle ABC = 180°$

TEST answers

5 AC is a diameter,
so ∠ABC = 90° (❺)
Then ∠BAC + ∠ACB = 90°
(angles in triangle)
Also ∠ACP = 90° (❶)
So ∠BCP + ∠ACB = 90°
Therefore ∠BAC = ∠BCP
But ∠BDC = ∠BAC (❻)
So ∠BCP = ∠BDC, where D is any point on
the circumference.

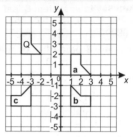

Page 90 Constructions & loci (1)
1 Check sides are 6 cm, angles are 60°
2 Check your line is 4 cm from each end and
at right angles
3 Check lines are at right angles

Page 91 Constructions & loci (2)
1 Check lines are at right angles
2 Check the two parts of the angle are 34°
3

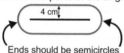
Ends should be semicircles

Page 92 Congruent & similar shapes (1)
1 **a** Congruent **b** Neither
2 x = 8 (s.f. is 2)

Page 93 Congruent & similar shapes (2)
1 **a** 1 : 16 **b** 1 : 64
2 See page 93.

Page 94 Vectors (1)
1 $-\mathbf{u} = \begin{bmatrix} 6 \\ -3 \end{bmatrix}$, $3\mathbf{p} - 2\mathbf{v} = \begin{bmatrix} 2 \\ -1 \end{bmatrix}$

2 $\begin{bmatrix} 6 \\ -3 \end{bmatrix} = 3 \begin{bmatrix} 2 \\ -1 \end{bmatrix}$

So $-\mathbf{u}$ is parallel to and 3 times as long
as $3\mathbf{p} - 2\mathbf{v}$.

Page 95 Vectors (2)
1 **a** x + y **b** -2y **c** y - x
2 13

Page 97 Transformations (2)
1 **a** Translation $\begin{bmatrix} -7 \\ 2 \end{bmatrix}$

b Reflection in the line y = x
c Rotation of 270° about (1, 0)
(or rotation of -90° about (1, 0)
or rotation of 90° clockwise about (1, 0))

2

Page 98 Transformations (3)
1

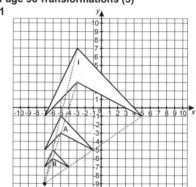

2 **a** Enlargement with centre (-1, 1), s.f. $\frac{1}{2}$
b Enlargement with centre (7, -3), s.f. 2

Page 99 Transformations (4)

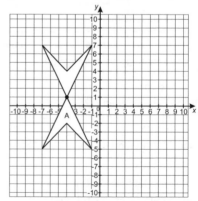

Page 100 Mean, median, mode, range
Mode = 1.2, Median = 5th ordered value = 1.2,
Mean = 9.9 ÷ 9 = 1.1, Range = 1.6 - 0.7 = 0.9

TEST answers

Page 101 Two-way tables; stem & leaf diagrams

1

	Black	Red	Blue	Total
Boys own	14	**1**	11	26
Girls own	7	7	**20**	34
Total	21	8	31	60

2

```
4 | 2 8 9
5 | 0 1 4 6 7 8 8 9
6 | 0 2 2 2 2 3 3 5 7 8 9 9
7 | 0 0 2 2 3 4 5
```
Key: 1|8 means 18

Page 102 Pie charts

1
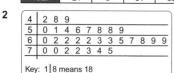
Other (40°)
Green (60°)
Red (160°)
Blue (100°)

2 Soaps: 9 students
Sport: 8 students
News: 3 students

Page 103 Time series & moving averages

2 About £98 seems reasonable
3 Using £98, the next M.A. is 74.5
4 Check trend line continues to go up slowly

Page 104 Averages from frequency tables (1)

1 1.8 pets (to 1 dp) **2** 2 cars **3** 2 cars

Page 105 Averages from frequency tables (2)

a

Height (h cm)	Tally	Frequency
$150 \leq h < 155$	I	1
$155 \leq h < 160$	IIII	4
$160 \leq h < 165$	III	3
$165 \leq h < 170$	⊬ III	8
$170 \leq h < 175$	II	2
$175 \leq h < 180$	II	2

b $3310 \div 20 = 165.5$ cm (midpoints: 152.5, etc)
c $165 \leq h < 170$ **d** $165 \leq h < 170$

Page 107 Frequency diagrams (2)

1 a

b
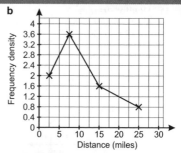

2

Height (cm)	0–	10–	15–	25–30
Frequency	8	11	14	7

Page 109 Cumulative frequency (2)

TV price (£P)	Frequency	Cumulative freq.
150–	3	3
200–	8	11
250–	12	23
300–	6	29
350–	1	30

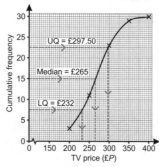

Median = £265, LQ = £232, UQ = £297.50
Interquartile range = £297.50 – £232 = £65.50

Page 110 Box plots

Minimum = 8, Maximum = 75
LQ = 14, UQ = 56, Median = 35

Page 111 Comparing sets of data

Histogram C is 'negatively skewed' (the majority of plants are 50–60 cm tall, with most of the rest shorter than this).
Both histograms show a 'narrow dispersion' (one bar much taller than the rest), which means the heights of the daffodils are quite consistent.

TEST answers

Page 112 Scatter graphs

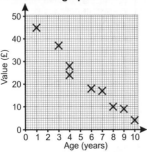

The graph shows strong negative correlation, i.e. value decreases as age increases.

Page 115 Probability (3)

1

		First dice				
		1	2	3	4	5	6
Second dice	1	1	2	3	4	5	6
	2	2	4	6	8	10	12
	3	3	6	9	12	15	18
	4	4	8	12	16	20	24
	5	5	10	15	20	25	30
	6	6	12	18	24	30	36

Probability of an even number = $\frac{27}{36} = \frac{3}{4}$

2 a $\frac{13}{52} = \frac{1}{4}$ **b** $1 - \frac{1}{13} = \frac{12}{13}$

c $\frac{26}{52} + \frac{1}{52} = \frac{27}{52}$

3 $\frac{1}{6} \times \frac{1}{6} = \frac{1}{36}$

4

1st biscuit	2nd biscuit	3rd biscuit

H = Hungry, N = Not hungry

The 'successful' outcomes are HHN, HNH and NHH.
P(HHN) or P(HNH) or P(NHH) =

$\frac{3}{5} \times \frac{2}{4} \times \frac{2}{3} + \frac{3}{5} \times \frac{2}{4} \times \frac{2}{3} + \frac{2}{5} \times \frac{3}{4} \times \frac{2}{3} = \frac{3}{5}$

Page 116 Surveys & sampling

1 a Options are too vague
  b Too personal
  c Leading question
2 a Perhaps assign each pupil a number, then randomly generate 50 numbers.
  b Randomly pick 30 Key Stage 3 pupils and 20 Key Stage 4 pupils.

Index

Index

Index